The Common Book
of Consciousness

W9-DBO-061

Diana Saltoon

The Common Book of Consciousness

*How To Take Charge of Your Lifestyle
Through Diet, Exercise and Meditation*

Introduction by Kenneth Pelletier

Illustrations by Amy Schwartz

Robert Briggs Associates

To Meda

Copyright © 1979 by Diana Saltoon.
All rights reserved.
Printed in the United States of America.

Fourth printing

SALTOON, DIANA.
The Common Book of Consciousness.

Bibliography: p. 149
Includes Index.
1. Consciousness.   2. Health.   3. Mental Health.
I. Title
BF311.S335   613   79-16069
ISBN 0-9609850-3-4

Book design by Patricia Girvin Dunbar.
Cover illustration by Susan Neri

Robert Briggs Associates
Box 9
Mill Valley
CA 94942

Table of Contents

Preface   7

Introduction   9

Intentions   13

Exercise and the Body   26

The Lifetime Diet   84

Relaxation and Meditation   105

Lifestyle   127

Bibliography   149

Preface

This book emerged from an instinctual need for change and was the result of much trial, error, and work toward an understanding of consciousness and the development of the four aspects of awareness. I found expanded consciousness to be a complex and profound goal and to define that goal demanded a simple and direct approach. Numerous books and various schools of thought provided theoretical information, but none furnished clear, simple methods of practice. There seemed no beginning, no outline, no basic step. The question became: what would I do *for* myself, before I did something *with* myself?

Becoming more whole and centered depended upon an integration of body, mind, spirit, and space which would provide the necessary change. This was easily accomplished through the realization of lifetime exercise, sane diet, the practice of meditation, and a more honest lifestyle. The difficulty was unifying these aspects in such a way as to produce wonder, experience of new security, and a greater command of the self. Hopefully, the sense of this vital unification is in the book.

In the process of this work I met many people who, knowingly or not, helped me along my way. I would like to mention a few: Jeff Longe, Ida Grylla, Mary and Louis S.B. Leakey, Hugo van Lawick, Ruth Layman, Judith Vanier, Ann Armstrong, Arthur M. Young, Sheila Krystal, Mad Bear and Jan Jones. As with most, 'this book could not have been written without' editorial help. Antoinette A. (Dolly) Gattozzi was a friend and wise consultant as well as an editor without parallel. I also wish to thank Sandor

Burstein for his expertise on "Wonderland," Frances Wilcox, Sharon Goodman, and Amy Schwartz for her illustrations.

Introduction

When English mathematician Lewis Carroll wrote *Alice in Wonderland,* he created a work of superb logic and classic social commentary. It is appropriate that Diana Saltoon has quoted from *Alice* in *The Common Book of Consciousness* since she has succeeded in presenting complex material concerning optimum health with great clarity through personal observation and practice. Since the early 1960s, individuals and institutions alike have come to realize the necessity of implementing a means for people to achieve and maintain health based upon lifestyle practices, but few pragmatic methods have been developed to achieve that end. This book is inspiring evidence that through "flexible yet persistent effort" an individual can live a lifetime of optimum health. Most importantly, this is a book by a woman who truly lives her philosophy while remaining in a demanding, "Western" job as a international stewardess with Trans World Airlines.

The Common Book of Consciousness is not a naive renunciation of any aspect of contemporary living. It is a sorting out of those aspects of our lifestyle that are necessary from those that are simply expedient. In the midst of Chapter Five concerning meditation, Ms. Saltoon juxtaposes insights derived from her practice to focus upon the issue of the "insidious infection" that the ubiquitous credit cards have induced in the lives of everyone. Throughout the book, lifestyle is viewed as the end result of many factors including exercise (for both cardiovascular toning as well as relaxation), diet and nutrition (including food preparation, which is frequently overlooked) and meditation, which serves as the primary means of unifying all the practices conducive to healthy lifestyle. The book realistically emphasizes that no combination of diet, exercise or meditation is a panacea. Its theme is that optimum health can be achieved only through unifying these practices in a "systematic, slow, and thoughtful" manner. The chapters are not intended to be didactic but rather serve as "guidelines" to "inspire your personal investigations of your individual requirements." This point cannot be emphasized enough, since there is no uniform prescription to develop an optimum lifestyle. There are only certain means to awaken an individual's awareness to realize, "a compassion for other people, other forms of life and for all things, and patience that arises from trusting in this path of wonder and change." While this ideal might seem far removed from our daily activity, it is an end that can be and has been attained.

Although the book is pleasantly personal it reflects many resources including C.G. Jung, the eminent biochemist Roger J. Williams, physicians Andrew Weil and Rudolph Ballentine, and philosopher Huston Smith to substantiate and hone insights into principles applicable to anyone seeking a more fulfilling existence. In Chapter Two, "Exercise and the Body," the instructions and illustrations are very clear and Ms. Saltoon's addition of personal experience lends a great deal of support to anyone seekng significant change. Each of the fourteen exercises has been uniquely adapted from yoga postures with the addition of some elements of aerobics. This synthesis is a characteristic of the entire book, which is never extreme in its guidelines since the thrust is to develop a style early in life that will persist and be applicable into extended longevity. There is a clear imperative for the consciousness of the individual to awaken to certain insights concerning diet rather than mechanically consuming a prescribed diet. At the outset Ms. Saltoon notes, "We must eliminate the concept of eating a certain way for a certain period of time before returning to the habits of consumption that caused trouble in the first place. . . . There can only be one diet! A final, lifetime diet." This is the clarity and wisdom necessary for fundamental life change. Such observations are well researched, succinctly stated, and followed by a range of specific means from the consideration of "seasonings and food preparation" to the complex issue of "periodic fasting." Finally, there is extensive consideration of the benefits of meditation after physical health has been implemented through nutrition and exercise.

Meditation, a complex subject, is rendered with superb clarity both in terms of the underlying philosophy and the specific postures and practices which are described. As to the eternal question of "why meditate," Ms. Saltoon observes: "The objective conditioning of the rational mind is necessary for survival in the material world, but merely to survive is not to live a fully human life. There is no mystery to materialism, but there is to human existence. Meditation illuminates the enigma." Again the subject of meditation is treated without the mystification, incense and robes. It is an inner experience inherently devoid of any trappings and can be and is frequently practiced today in the corporate boardroom as well as the isolated retreat for the same purpose: "to know who you are." The answer to that question is possible, and, once known, serves as the unifying principle which binds together the separate aspects of a lifestyle of optimum fulfillment. The wisdom in *The Common Book of Consciousness* is accessible to everyone who has questioned the meaning of personal existence.

On her houseboat in the San Francisco Bay Diana Saltoon lives the message of her book. Through a personal transformation she has found the means to convey this "systematic framework" to everyone who seeks to "meet an inner demand for more complete and fulfilling lives." In clinical practice and research I am constantly asked to formulate such approach. Now it is possible to give a tangible resource: Diana Saltoon's *The Common Book of Consciousness*.

Kenneth R. Pelletier
San Francisco, California
April of 1979

CHAPTER ONE

Intentions

Would *you tell me, please*
which way I ought to go from here?"

"That depends a good deal on where you want to get to. . . .

Alice in Wonderland

The Common Book of Consciousness offers an integrated and practical system that can help you develop greater awareness and lead you toward higher understanding. Through this awareness we become capable of more knowledgeable responses to life. We begin a new appreciation of the world in which we live, both inside and outside of our skins. In the system provided here awareness is developed through a combination of exercise, a control of what you consume, by learning how to relieve stress and to tap the wellspring of your being through meditation, and by gradually altering lifestyle.

The Common Book of Consciousness is for those who seek true change, who accept the necessity of a lifetime exercise program, and who have begun to see the gradual suicide that comes with careless eating habits. It is for those who recognize the pervasive, insidious dangers of stress and understand the need for true relaxation of body and mind. It is for those who sense their spiritual nature, and have begun to confront the need to alter the context of their lives, the places in which they dwell, in order to promote healthful change and allow themselves new growth.

I believe that increasing awareness in the four quarters of your daily life — body, mind, spirit and the space in which this three-in-one you lives — leads naturally to a higher understanding of the meaning of your life. As your personal consciousness becomes harmoniously integrated it is discovered to be far greater than the sum of its parts; it connects you with the cosmic consciousness that animates all the things that participate in our living world. However, the immediate and practical reward for developing awareness in these four aspects is that you will become physically, mentally, and emotionally healthier, more centered, stable and sound, yet more flexible and adaptable to life as well. You will be more alive and live a better life. I see these four quarters as the mighty landmarks of the domain of consciousness. By developing awareness of body, mind, and spirit, and by cultivating a total harmonious ecology of the self, we honor consciousness within ourselves and all around us.

This book attempts to sort out the widespread (but frequently half thought out) interest in health, diet, meditation, relief of stress and other partial schemes of self-help that are so topical today. It seeks to demonstrate correlations within these interests and the idea of increasing one's awareness, deeper inner understanding and self-actualization. One of the most vital points to grasp is that the four areas of daily life noted above are tightly related. To be cognizant of the need for physical health, yet to ignore the subject of meditation is an approach ultimately doomed to failure by omission. Similarly, it is shortsighted and futile to practice meditation regularly, yet neglect the environment provided by your home and on the job. And so on. Developing awareness in any one or two or even three areas may bring some positive results but they will be short-lived fragments of what one could attain.

The key to using *The Common Book of Consciousness* successfully is to recognize the seamless unity of consciousness and the consequent necessity of dealing with yourself and your life *as a whole*. That may sound like a grand order but it is certainly not beyond you if you are willing to learn. This book will help you gradually to define, work for, and eventually achieve your aims. It offers a *systematic* framework for seeing and changing the way we live now as we instinctively strive to meet an inner demand for more complete and fulfilling lives: lives lived with imagination and wonder; lives that allow you to know yourself and to fulfill your potentials; lives shot through with glimpses of and long moments spent in the harmony and flow of grander realities than those now experienced.

The past decade has been unique in stirring questions about *consciousness*. On the intellectual level, for example, the University of California at Santa Barbara recently brought together scholars and scientists for a seminar on consciousness, stating that "the inner world of the human mind and spirit and the physical and natural universe are beginning to be understood as intimately related to each other." This realization "has profound implications for personal transformation, health, psychotherapy, religion, philosophy, parapsychology, and the arts."

On the popular level, George Gallup reported in February, 1978, that "one of the most remarkable trends in the 1970s is the continuing interest in the inner, or spiritual, life." His pollsters found that a projected fifty-six million Americans were involved in various religious disciplines and movements. The academic ferment and wide-ranging experimentation have aroused many millions more to examine their personal sphere of consciousness with a view toward expansion and heightening. But despite the great number of books and articles that have been circulated and the far-flung operations of the motley consciousness-raising industry, there has been a sorry failure to define those aspects that are of immediate relevance to common, ordinary life and to lay out the basic information needed for personal transformation.

This book is an attempt to do just that. It is designed as a primer for people who want to devote time to activity that will help change the major habits which determine the quality of living.

Today the concern for improving one's physical condition is evident in the burgeoning popularity of jogging and other aerobic activities. What and what not to eat have become an American obsession. This is evidence of a healthy impulse in our society toward self-improvement—although the time when it will come to fruition in the decades ahead is impossible to tell.

Nevertheless, the coast-to-coast interest in exercise and diet is a healthy sign. As the chief public health officer of the United States told a meeting of the American Medical Association in the summer of 1978, too many Americans have long been leading self-destructive lives. Calling on all citizens, Health, Education and Welfare Secretary Joseph Califano said, "We must replace our prevailing ethic of expensive self-indulgence with an ethic of personal responsibility."

To be fit, to be thin, and to abstain from drugs is patriotic, even a social asset. The interest in conserving and wisely using natural resources is global in scope. The health of our planet earth is at stake as the emergencies of pollution and exploitation are worldwide.

These few examples serve to illustrate that certain tremendous forces are coming to bear *simultaneously,* and that tens of millions of Americans are moving into processes of momentous personal change, adding up to sweeping changes in society. At the center of this much-maligned, often-misunderstood "consciousness movement" are you and your own instinct to develop awareness and rid your life of self-imposed tyrannies: destructive or futile habits of body and mind; spiritual stagnation; and negative lifestyle. These parts are all of a piece and the piece is you. Tinkering, dabbling, or even devotedly concentrating on one or a few of the parts can be moves made in the right direction if they awaken you to a vision of the wholeness that totally supports your life. However vague or fleeting, that vision will inspire you—as it did me—to take on the whole challenge of your human potential.

For this goal, a *unified* program for the development of awareness is imperative. It is not enough just to "get more exercise" or "cut down" on what you eat. "Getting away from it all" can actually increase your stress levels if you do it without knowing how to relax. Buying some plants and spending a "little more time on yourself" can be lonely and pointless unless you have created an atmosphere in which there is a place for a scheme of personal growth, a place in which you can practise a complete ecology of the self. Only to the extent that you have the courage and the sincerity of purpose to stride toward wholeness will you fully satisfy the soundest instinct of your life.

The Common Book of Consciousness is not exhaustive in covering all the information available, nor is it meant to be definitive. It reflects a seasoned and personal point of view. It is a handbook for a complete and basic system of life practices, which develops awareness and expands consciousness, the particulars of which can be suited to the reader's individual needs. What we do determines the quality of our lives, and I believe that we are destined to refine our lives in order that "something more" may arise in our awareness.

It all began for me a dozen years ago when I lived in New York City and, through curiosity and chance, was introduced to yoga. I will never forget meeting my first teacher of hatha yoga. Ida was about sixty yet she glowed with health and vitality. Her physical poise and posture were those of a much younger woman; certainly her agility exceeded my own in gracefulness and strength.

I was intrigued. If yoga could prevent the usual deleterious effects of aging then it was for me! It was not just the surface aspect of a vividly healthful appearance, it was her total presence. There was a relaxed alertness, an alive patience, a tolerance blended with warmth and compassion that endeared her to me. I longed to be able to age as gracefully as she had.

It took several years to discover that exercise in itself (what I learned as the hatha limb of the classical eight-limbed yoga), would change nothing. Doing yogic exercises did reduce my weight and make my body more limber. Afterwards I felt relaxed and, for a short while, energized. But, by returning to my old habits and hectic schedules, I did not experience any lasting change. Yogic exercise was a magnificent discipline but, by itself, did not induce the change I had hoped would come. It caused me to become newly aware of my body but it did not alter the total sense of my life. Nevertheless the exercises were the the first step to my realization that more — and less — was needed.

I say less because it gradually dawned that, like almost everyone else, I was eating and drinking too much and often consumed items of little or no nutritional value. Exercise, the first line of body awareness, led me to a careful consideration of my eating habits and the discovery that the two are highly interactive. Later I came to see that both foods and the external impressions I consumed deliberately (or was exposed to willy-nilly by the circumstances of daily life) greatly affected me both physically and mentally. As awareness of these needs increased and began to be met, another dimension of myself came increasingly into focus as a vital part of the whole. I refer to the spiritual nature which abides in each of us. Learning to tend and cultivate this aspect of life through meditation seems to me to lie at the very heart of the yearning for completion and fulfillment. Lastly I realized that awareness and refinement of my inner spaces of body, mind, and spirit required control of my outer environment, the spaces in which I lived my daily life, the elements that comprised my lifestyle.

These learning experiences took place over the course of many years. I am not certain at what point I realized that I was a "closet" student of consciousness, nor is this important except to point out that I have always considered myself, and been thought of by others, as a woman leading a life not atypical of my time and place. I have always been a working woman and have, as it happens, a career as an airline stewardess which I find rewarding. Constant travel to international cities gradually illuminated the gross failings of my American diet. That diet, combined with the strain of jet lag, eventually produced serious physical consequences that had to be dealt with. Having neither the inclination nor the time for deep study and research I simply learned what I could from eclectic reading and trusted my intuition to guide me forward at a pace commensurate with my needs and capacities. I believe that this was right and proper, and I know that it has been effective.

The subject of yoga is wide and deep. According to the Sanskrit scholar Jean Varenne, the word "yoga" should be understood as meaning "magic recipe," or "method." Certainly the yogic recipe is of great complexity and subtlety, and in looking to it for direction and clues on how to define and proceed toward my goals, I was very impressed but also put off. It seemed extreme: too specific and almost contradictory to what I was and how I wished to live. I wanted to improve my life through change but not to alter it radically. I did not want to withdraw. I admired the philosophy of yoga but found the severity of its discipline to be impractical.

Meanwhile, I carried on with the exercises and gradually adapted and shaped them into the sets and series that produced the maximum beneficial effects for me. The second chapter of this book outlines the program I devised. The movements are primarily based on hatha yoga exercises and the program is designed to serve for a lifetime. It rejects athleticism, for I believe that—unless you are paid to do otherwise as athletes are—you should exercise with a lifetime aim of maintaining health and preventing the needless debilities that too often accompany aging. To develop unnecessary muscularity is ridiculous. It is useless off the field and outside of real (or imagined) competitive situations.

In Chapter Three I suggest a final, lifetime diet designed to free the user from the traditional means of diet control, which are not only impractical but actually destructive to anyone intent upon living a full life. There are no more than a dozen simple principles concerning what and how much to eat in order to obtain the nutrition and energy that one needs. These are presented here along with pointers on cooking and meal planning as well as on fasting. In addition to what is eaten, your daily diet consists of all your practices involving food, and a primary aim of the final lifetime diet is to bring you back to the sources of food whereby you see the preparation and consumption of food as a vital part of body-mind awareness.

Beginning to exercise regularly and eat properly leads naturally to an active concern about stress, for stress-related psychosomatic disorders are everywhere among us. Stress that becomes *distress* is one of the most pervasive killing factors of our time. It is an indirect and, in many cases, a direct contributor to car accidents and other acts of social violence as well as to the cancers, heart attacks, ulcers, respiratory ailments and other diseases which plague the middle and later years of almost all Americans.

Chapter Four deals with meditation, the *key* to profoundly restorative relaxation. A daily habit of meditation is not only an excellent antidote to stress but—as this chapter will show—it brings us in contact with that essential sense of ourselves we often, sadly, seem to have lost.

Lifestyle is the area of concern covered in Chapter Five, which discusses the possibilities for creating fruitful private lives and escaping traps of materialism and authoritarianism. It is foolhardy for anyone to attempt drastic or abrupt changes in her or his lifestyle. After some years of difficult and sometimes hilarious or embarrassing experiences I can vouch for the great subtlety required to change your lifestyle.

To improve health one can exercise and change eating habits. To relax and gain great psychic and psychological centeredness one can meditate. These practices produce immediate and direct effects. But there are no prescriptions for changing lifestyle. Instead, it simply happens more or less as follows: the practices related to exercise, consumption and meditation entrain a process of unification through which your lifestyle has already begun to change. Attitudes and practices are the foundation of change. Next, the home needs to be seen as a total environment which must be critically appraised and appropriately altered. Lastly, interactions with society and its institutions need to be carefully considered. These are the elements that determine the quality of private life, and it is within private life that awareness is best developed. This chapter suggests ways in which you can support and foster the three basic activities of daily awareness: exercise, consumption, and meditation. The styles of your inner attitudes and outer environments dominate the way you live moment-to-moment.

Awareness of lifestyle is no less vital to consciousness than is physical fitness, proper nutrition and psycho-spiritual centeredness. Cultivating awareness in all four fields is the key to *The Common Book of Consciousness.*

The greatest decisions of human life have as a rule far more to do with the instincts and other mysterious unconscious factors than with the conscious will and well-meaning reasonableness. The shoe that fits one person pinches another; there can be no recipe for the living that suits all cases. Each of us carries his own life form—an indeterminable form which cannot be superseded by an other.

Carl Gustav Jung

The dynamics of a unified practice of awareness are powerful. They entail physical, psychic, and social consequences that are of incalculable benefit to the person who follows them. Yet such practices are not narcissistic or selfish. I believe that goodness proceeds from within as surely as it flows from without. It is still rightly said that charity begins at home—so too with understanding and love. We are responsible for ourselves and ought to fulfill that task in the most intelligent and deeply caring way. I think that the present American interest in awareness and consciousness comes from an instinctual recognition on the part of millions that there is something more, something better for each one of us. It is a recognition that bodes well for our collective future.

We ought not to continue to plod through the old patterns. The historian Theodore Roszak has written that "we desperately need to outgrow the dismal and diminished human image we inherit from the past two centuries of industrialism. We need a radically altered conception of ourselves, our primary needs, of our place in nature...."

I say we grow from within, and I say that it is in our human potential to know ourselves and our full destiny. Besides, to me it is painfully obvious that the society in which we live does not cherish individual lives. The authorities that control it have far more invested in sowing and reaping the technological and materialistic jungle in which most of us are trapped. The practice of unified awareness is like a path through the jungle. It is the means whereby the individual regains command of her or his life.

The charges of narcissim, of being of the "me-generation" of the politically uncaring, often sound like the Establishment East taking to task the New Age West. Thus, Senator George McGovern mourned the passage of the California initiative on property tax relief as an example of its voters' "degrading hedonism." The strong prejudice against trying for new solutions often uses ridicule and frequently is politically or economically motivated. Whatever the complicated case may be, I have found the charges absurd, for I have been able to exercise and meditate regularly, stay well nourished on a modest budget, and define my needs and priorities without losing my allegiances to community and country or giving up my personal relationships. All of this was done without dropping out in any sense, without escaping those family, social, and political duties that may face any woman or man.

According to Tarthang Tulku, a contemporary Master of Tibetan Buddhism, "We can be 'selfish' in taking care of ourselves...by making our minds and bodies as harmonized as possible." At the same time as you come to accept and appreciate yourself, you become open to compassion for others. He writes, "Through the integration and balancing of our minds and bodies, it is possible to attain the inner peace and joy which is love itself." Love is the ultimate flower of living consciousness and to live in love and become love is to merge with your spirit. You travel a circle and come back to this core of yourself. It is a journey that merges with wisdom. By living consciousness we open ourselves to love, the genius of our species. We open our own doors of perception and develop the intuitive and psychic abilities that are part of our heritage. We go beyond toward the development of psychic power and understanding. These perceptions strengthen our centers with trust and further expand our consciousness. As the mystery reveals itself we see we are each a single thread woven into a cosmic pattern that is beyond intellectual comprehension or verbal statement. To gaze is to see but a segment. The pattern extends into never-ending cycles of creation and degeneration. Through awareness we spin our own thread and knowingly participate in a mandala of life. We free the spirit and let it soar. With love as a companion we feel invincible.

The lives most of us lead are contained and conditioned. Freedom consists of setting the spirit free. All of us are endowed with this noblest of intentions. To carry it out requires developing awareness and taking control of our lives. "We learn by doing!" says a Jonathan Winters character at the end of a particularly droll routine. Our confusions are often deeply confounding, but we must not take things too seriously nor doubt that we are smart enough to meet the requirements. Much of what is called learning is a kind of rediscovery of things already known although long since forgotten. Once you have begun a unified practice of awareness you will know how to proceed toward final goals and you will have the means to get there. Whether you tarry to seek past lives, to see death, or to find a guru is up to you, of course, but I urge you to stay focused on everyday, ordinary life throughout any search.

The guidelines offered in *The Common Book of Consciousness* are simple in conception and straightforward in presentation. Few of you will be unfamiliar with the elements offered here; some might consider them simplistic. Certainly the points developed in this book are intellectually simple. A line I read recently summing up a harrowing adventure novel by Lionel Davidson strikes me as being relevant: "If experience taught anything it was not to think too much, but to sharpen up the responses." Many people waste fine time thinking about, brooding over their dwindling vitality, stale routines, sterile pursuits, and the superficiality of their lives. To wrestle abstractly with complex propositions and large philosophical issues will exercise the intellect but it will not change one's life. The purpose of this book is to help you choose and effect change from which anyone can develop her or his own diversity. The object is to show you a unified way toward personal exploration, growth, and transcendence.

Live in each season as it
*passes; breathe the air; drink the drink, taste the fruit
and resign yourself to the influence of each. Let them be
your only diet, drink and botanical medicines. Be blown
on by all the winds. Open all your pores and bathe in all
the tides of nature, in all her streams and oceans, at all
seasons."*

Henry David Thoreau

Different fashions have been attached to the development of awareness. One aspect that has always been emphasized is the naturalness of this endeavor, as the lines from Thoreau indicate. Although some people feel it is necessary to seek quietude by dropping out of society in order to achieve expanded consciousness, I disagree. For most of these people such a course is fraught with confusion and can end in disappointment. We all know one or more of the antisocial, burnt-out cases. To drop out by surrendering to religious life, taking up psychedelic drug use, even moving to a farming commune—to name but a few of the most notorious instances—can provoke psychological and cultural shocks that tend to distort awareness rather than enhance it.

Awareness is as natural to the human condition as breathing. Awareness can be developed virtually any place at any time by anyone of any age. The suburb or the outlying district is as adequate as the metropolitan setting. No rare expertise need be sought. No special group or religion is needed. After developing a habit of regular exercise and learning to control consumptions, after forming a solid meditative habit and coordinating this with your own command of silence and privacy, spirituality will come in the form you need. Too often the practical elicitation of one's spiritual nature is thought to be dependent upon one or another religious discipline. This is not necessarily so. By unifying the tangible activities you bring together mind and body and prepare the ground for spiritual awakening and growth.

Being natural and utterly immediate, the practice of awareness does not exclude any aspect of life nor neglect historical continuity. Yogi Sujit has stated, "Cosmic consciousness is worthless without social consciousness...

we must re-charge our energies to go back to the battlefield of life, not escape," while Yogi Vishnu Devananda reminds us: "Many are working today for the promotion of world peace without first having peace within themselves. How can the blind help the blind? This world can be saved only by those who have already saved themselves." In short, those who make accusations of narcissism fail to see that individual psychosomatic / psycho-spiritual unity is the source of beneficial social change.

Nor is this practice easy, despite its ordinariness. There is no glamour or sensationalism about unifying the four quarters of consciousness. To develop awareness and fulfill one's human potential requires patience and sincere effort.

We look to the earth and sift sands in the hope of uncovering clues that throw light on the origin and purpose of our existence. We look to the heavens for deliverance. By directing effort toward increasing awareness I believe we can find what we seek.

Students of consciousness, what some also call spiritual explorers, regularly appear throughout history. The practice of unifying awareness and enlarging personal consciousness toward the goal of transcendence is humankind's Primordial Tradition, to use the designation given it by the historian Huston Smith. In the past, the overwhelming majority of these individuals led lives as common and ordinary as you and I do. A few of them—poets, scholars, spiritual masters, thinkers and artists—have left records of their experience that we can use in our own studies. (No committee wrote *The Bhagavad Gita* or fashioned the formula "$E = mc^2$.") One by one, we gladly join them on the bedrock of reality. And we find many others there similarly occupied. They are related to us in many different ways but basically they are our co-teachers and co-students. One by one, we are all engaged on the same noble task.

To go beyond the ordinary realms of expectation you must be willing to explore the *terra incognita*—the unknown country—of the mind. Extra-sensory perceptions and other psychic phenomena are but a part of what exists within the mind. These will not concern us here. Scientists know a great lot of bits and pieces about the brain and nervous system but this too is excluded from consideration here because they can tell us virtually nothing about the mind. Psychologist Robert Ornstein admitted that academic psychology has for the past sixty years refused to study the essential questions of its discipline. These questions are, he wrote in the preface to his book of readings called *The Nature of Human Consciousness:* "How does the mind work? What are the major dimensions of human consciousness? Is consciousness individual or cosmic? What means are there to extend human consciousness?" We can only wish him and all of his like-minded colleagues well in their efforts to reform a bankrupt operation.

My program of developing awareness is frankly optimistic in outlook while remaining clear-eyed about the many pitfalls and dead ends that stymie the beginner. As awareness increases you experience the truth that you are constantly evolving to fulfill a universal scheme of totality. To celebrate the joy of complete and total life, to realize the whole of our potential requires you to enter that inner unknown country and trustingly step into other realms of human existence far more spacious, wonderous, and drenched in reality than those to which we are accustomed. The feast is prepared: the celebration begins when you embark.

CHAPTER TWO

Exercise and the Body

Of the three factors deter-
*mining a person's general behavior, self-education alone
is appreciably subject to will. The question is really to
what extent and, most particularly, in what way one can
help oneself. . . . Self-help is the only way open to everyone.
The way is hard and complicated, but for every person
who feels the need for change and improvement, it is
within the limits of practical possibility.*

Moshe Feldenkrais
Awareness Through Movement

I.

The body comes first. A whole and healthy body is a great gift, and maintaining sound physical health the most basic responsibility we have. So much depends upon realizing that health is a condition that can be improved and controlled. So much else depends on it.

In recent years doctors and public health officials have been urgently advising the public that a person's daily practices in the areas of exercise and diet strongly influence the current status and future course of their physical health. The research findings clearly show that whether or not you will enjoy a long and vigorously healthy lifetime depends primarily on how you choose to live today. Meeting your body's daily needs for exercise and proper nutrition is the first line of defense against the encroachment of those debilitating diseases so tragically characteristic of middle and later decades of life. Freedom from infirmity is certainly important to the body's well-being which is, in turn, the physical frame wherein the person's psychosomatic and psycho-spiritual selves take being. The physical and nonphysical aspects of your whole self are thought to be totally interpenetrating. Nevertheless, it makes sense from the point of view of self-education to start with the most obvious, easily perceived aspect—literally, the living material of one's human organism, one's body. That is what makes exercise and diet the starting points of any effort to unify the development of awareness.

A healthy body is fit, flexible, and able to relax. Muscles are in tone; breathing and blood circulation are efficient; joints and tendons are pliable; and the stresses of everyday life are regularly relieved through deep relaxation. Beyond this a healthy person is one who is conscious of—and feels a sense of solidarity with—her or his body. They are in touch with their body, and between the mind and body there is trust and cooperation. In this way the fundamental psychosomatic unity of human life is given positive expression. Healthy persons also have a rich appreciation of personal reality, of being here and now in the physical world. Yet, surprisingly, this feeling of solidity and substance does not have the effect of weighing them down.

The opposite is true.

As physical health improves and mind-body integrity enlarges, the quality of physical energy changes. It becomes lighter, clearer, more abundant, and somehow more intelligent. This is the expression of the psycho-spiritual aspect of human nature. In sum, the optimally healthy person is one who is functioning harmoniously in body, mind and spirit.

Only a small portion of all people are optimally healthy. A much larger fraction are frankly ill and in need of medical care. Even among the great majority who have no clear-cut health problems, there is always room for improvement. The way to begin moving toward optimum health is to cultivate a daily habit of exercise and disciplined movement that both promotes physical health and develops body awareness. The next stage is entered when you realize that what you eat affects not only the health of your body but also the quality of your energy. Permanently changing your eating habits for the better is the goal of the lifetime diet presented in the following chapter. Learning how to allow the physical body deeply restorative relaxation and, beyond that, to free the spirit for exploration of other worlds of consciousness is the third stage, and the final stage deals with putting all this together into a personally satisfying lifestyle. In my experience, every stage is vital to the whole development and none is secondary or subordinate to the others.

Nevertheless, we have to start somewhere and build from there, and I believe that it is best to start with directly caring for the physical body. Attend to the body's need for exercise by establishing a discipline, creating an exercise program for yourself that is efficient and enjoyable.

The fourteen exercises offered here have been freely adapted from yoga postures with the addition of some elements from Western-style calisthenics. They are designed to enable you gradually to bring your body into awareness while increasing its suppleness and vigor. No matter the size and shape of your body, how much or how little exercise you have done in the past, no matter what your particular physical limitations might be, anyone can devise a suitable program from the series and sets suggested. The emphasis should be on *how* you do each exercise rather than how many exercises you perform. Do those you most enjoy but always work on others you have not yet mastered. Always challenge yourself a little bit more. The exercises should never seem boring. They should never tire you; rather they should please and invigorate. Be patient in learning the details of the movements and allow yourself to enjoy what you are doing for yourself.

These exercise routines are not for the athletically minded. I feel that the aims of athletic competitiveness are antagonistic to those of people who wish to exercise for a longer, better life. Athletes exercise to harden their bodies and develop muscularity, and they concentrate on developing or over-developing bodily skills in order to compete against others. Such training is not congenial to the unification and wholeness needed to support longevity. Athleticism also conditions the body in ways that can cause increased food consumption, which is hardly a desirable outcome.

By contrast, swimming, jogging, and bicycling done for exercise and pleasure offer excellent benefits. They are vigorous whole-body activities that efficiently condition the cardiovascular and respiratory systems, thereby improving the heart and blood circulation among other good effects. These are ideal activities for anyone interested in a long and healthy life. The critical elements of an active, vibrant old age are a flexible spine and sound heart and lungs. Maintaining efficient circulation of oxygen-rich blood throughout the body is the key to preventing senility. This is the direction we shall take.

One reason jogging has become so popular lately is that it needs no costly equipment or special facilities and can be done alone. At last estimate, twenty million Americans were said to be jogging regularly. For the same reason, walking turns out to be the favorite form of exercise for Americans aged twenty or more, according to the National Center for Health Statistics. I myself prefer long, brisk walks to the other, more vigorous whole-body exercises. Although walking is more time-consuming, I find it far more pleasurable, and I believe that enjoyment is the key to a lifetime exercise program.

There is another class of whole-body exercises that are not as widely appreciated although equally vital to health. Such exercises are generally done indoors and in private, and they call forth a different kind of discipline. Recognizing another class of exercise calls attention to the body's need for subtle-sense, integrative activity. The need for integrating or harmoniously tuning the finer levels of physical functioning is less obvious, but not less important to health and longevity, than the vigorous conditioning of the heart and lung systems. The fourteen exercises presented in this chapter belong in this class of integrative exercise.

In creating your own program you will do well to include both vigorous and integrative types of exercise. If you already jog or swim for exercise and wish to capitalize fully on these activities, I urge you to begin practicing the exercises offered here. Everyone can enhance his or her well-being by making these exercises a part of one's daily life. This is easier than you might imagine, for they can be performed no matter the weather or season or time of day. As little as twenty minutes a day, with almost no time needed for preparation or winding down, can make a successful beginning program.

Most significantly, the exercises call for slow, careful execution and great concentration. They are ideal for people beginning on a path of unified self-knowledge, for people who not only wish to be physically fit but also want to develop greater awareness of their bodies. This is the direction toward freeing the mind-body for other awareness.

The most important advantage of following the routines presented here is that you are working on three levels simultaneously. On one level you stretch muscles and improve circulation; you are taking the gentle path to becoming physically fit. On the second, you are practicing body awareness, enhancing inner sensibilities, tuning to the joyful sounds of life within your skin; you are on a path leading to optimum health. On the third level you are systematically learning to relax in that each exercise calls for mild tension, with awareness, followed by brief rest. And each practice session should end with the deeply relaxing exercise I call Going Within, which is marvelously effective for relieving all kinds of damaging effects of stress. This exercise also prepares a quiet body state, a meditative stillness in which you begin to intuit a center of utter calm deep inside yourself. At the third level, then, you are on a path of spiritual freedom.

Too few people realize the crucial importance of knowing how to relax completely, right down into the bones. From the health point of view, physicians are coming to agree with Elmer and Alyce Green of the Menninger Foundation when they say, "It is not life that kills us, rather it is our reaction to it, and this reaction can be to a considerable extent self-chosen." Stress that is *not* relieved through deep relaxation becomes distress, which leads to *dis-ease*. Deep relaxation, regularly practiced, is what we can choose as our response to the daily stresses we often relish but which threaten to get the better of us if we let them tick away, like so many time bombs, under our skin. Such potentially damaging stress effects are very neatly defused by deep relaxation. You cannot do your body, or yourself, a greater favor than this.

Also, most people do not appreciate the active role of awareness in relaxation. True relaxation requires the withdrawal of attention from the on-going movie show of daily life. The movies continue, of course, but one directs attention elsewhere, to more subtle and more immediate concerns. Gathering the attention to an inward focus and quieting the body happen together. In short, true relaxation is a body-and-mind event.

All this will become clear as you gradually learn and regularly practice the exercises in this chapter. In so doing you make a firm beginning to changing your life, being and becoming the person you wish to be, on the three levels described above. Chapter Four takes up from here and suggests ways to develop other practices of the third level, the path of spiritual freedom. In that chapter you will find many pointers on sitting meditation and other forms of focused attention.

There is one mini-exercise for relaxation that I want to outline before turning to the routines which will make up your structured program. I call it Taking a Breather. It can be done anywhere at any time. In fact, I especially recommend doing it when you are with other people—on the job, at a desk or during rest and meal breaks; in the kitchen with the family; in the living room with friends; on a bus or in a restaurant. It takes only a moment and will do wonders. It goes as follows:

TAKING A BREATHER

While seated, let your gaze drop to an easy-feeling point in midspace. Then, relax your face: feel the skin of the forehead and around the eyes let go; feel the cheeks and lips untense. As you do this, now take a full breath, exhaling slowly, and gently straighten your posture so that you are not twisted or slumped; have your hands on your lap. Keep your lips closed and breathe through your nose. Continue being aware of full, comfortable breathing and of a relaxed face.

The key to a relaxed face is relaxed teeth! When what the dentists call your bite is relaxed, your teeth are just barely not touching. Gently put them in that position while you continue breathing. Relaxed teeth indicate a relaxed jaw. Now your whole head and face are momentarily relieved of the tensions brought about by social interaction. For just a moment or two, you are restored to yourself, you go to the wellspring within, take a breather, then rejoin the others with renewed gusto for participation, interaction and cooperation.

If you can take another moment or so, carry on with relaxing the whole of your upper body. Starting with the feeling of that

---

relaxed jaw, feel the neck muscles relax and let go from below the ears and under the jaw right out to the tips of each shoulder. Continue breathing and feel the shoulder blades on your back, your upper arms and upper chest relax. Please do not sag. This would interfere with free and full breathing, which is the main feature of this exercise. Finally, let go of tension in the lower arms, wrists and hands. Continue breathing and being aware of a relaxed face and upper body.

This exercise for practicing relaxation complements the one I call Going Within, and both are linked to the meditation postures and practices outlined in a later chapter. Although Going Within may seem unfamiliar, I believe that a great many people already do one variant or another of Taking a Breather. It is really so simple and common-sensical. Basically, one sits still and breathes. By investing this natural act with conscious attention, one can add great power to its benefits. Among other splendid effects, this simple exercise in self-regulation increases self-confidence and social poise.

Like breathing, waking is a natural act we almost always perform automatically. We seldom consider that the act of waking from a night's sleep is subject to increased awareness and change. By the time a person has reached the age of thirty years she or he has begun nearly 11,000 days; by fifty years old, has awakened to more than 18,000. "Beginning the new day" becomes so automatic it seems absurd to consider how it is done. Yet the last moments of sleep, the transition between sleep and wakefulness, is a time of rare importance. How it is experienced influences how we live. No matter what problems are to be faced, what trials the day may bring, waking is a time for brief inward focus on the sense of that gap between the end of one state of consciousness and beginning of another. Waking is crucial and not to be overlooked nor excluded from change. The mechanics of waking is simple, but what is important is not mechanical or simple. It is learning *why* a sympathetic procedure of waking is necessary. The why emerges as you make changes and observe their effects. How to improve waking is as follows.

ON AWAKENING

Care for yourself as you emerge from sleep. Remain quiet a moment or two after the alarm. It is best to train yourself to awaken naturally at a given time and dispense with the use of an alarm. The most important thing is not to be jarred from sleep or to bolt out of bed. Tune in to your breathing. Breathe, stretch and gently roll your body from side to side. On rising swing both legs to the floor and lift your weight onto both feet equally. If the details of a dream seem significant, take a moment to jot them down.

This is an excellent time for meditation. However, you may want to meditate later and exercise instead. A jog in the early morning clears the head and quickens the blood. It is a splendid way to begin, but not everyone can or will jog daily. A pregnancy or business trip can interrupt a morning exercise habit, but nothing should disrupt the private moments of waking. Whatever your personal arrangements try always to make your waking moments a time of intimate centeredness.

People often say, "I don't have time to exercise!" Yet we have time to see friends and even those who sour us or add little to our lives. We spend time needlessly shopping and waste hours on trivial errands. Why then is it so difficult to devote thirty minutes or an hour to yourself alone? So little time is spent on the self that we must question, who are we living for? To live a life of awareness you must begin by accepting the responsibility of caring for your body. No one else will do it for you; no one can. To build and maintain health and purity is not vain or selfish. It is the first step in living more fully and freeing your energy so that you may better serve others. We begin by devoting time to the body, and in so doing we use our right to change what we are and seek what we want to become.

II.

Select the routines of your personal program from the fourteen exercises presented in this section. Read each one through carefully and look closely at the accompanying illustrations. As you do so, try to visualize yourself moving as indicated, step by step. Don't actually carry out the instructions at this time, but do pause during your reading and try to imagine the torso, limbs and head of your own body moving in prescribed ways. Moshe Feldenkrais, developer of a highly effective system of physical rehabilitation, has repeatedly demonstrated the power of visualization in his work with thousands of patients and students. Visualizing your body moving as instructed, in the absence of any contrary feedback arising from the body's current limitations, guarantees success in the psychic aspect of your psychosomatic self. True, you probably will practice many weeks before your physical body totally responds to the commands of your will. Nevertheless, it is extremely useful at the very start to see yourself in your mind's eye moving with beautiful precision and control.

Fourteen Exercises

1. Sun Series
2. For the Legs
3. Rocking
4. Headstand
5. Shoulder Stand
6. A Half Fish
7. Plow
8. Plow Combination
9. The Rise
10. For the Stomach
11. Breathing
12. For the Eyes
13. For the Neck
14. Going Within

You are ready to begin practicing when you have reserved a half-hour for exercise in your daily schedule. It can be early morning, right before bed, during a work break if your work place provides adequate space, or after work and before dinner. Fit in the half-hour (or more) whenever it suits you. Begin with the Sun Series, and proceed to perform all the exercises, which may require two or three practice sessions. Then select seven routines you want to master first and concentrate on them for the time being. I recommend the following sequence of exercises for the beginner: Sun Series; Leg Exercises; Rocking; Breathing; For the Eyes; Neck Exercises; Going Within. When you have memorized the details of these exercises and practiced them for several weeks, add or substitute one or more of the remaining exercises. Keep incorporating new routines and rotating the total fourteen until, within six months, you have learned all of them. From this point on, the pleasure of daily practice and the dramatic mind-body improvement you experience will have made your program an integral part of your life.

Believing is seeing; believe you can make profoundly beneficial changes in your physical body, then act on this belief and see for yourself.

Go easy; never strain. There is no hurry, no time limit; there are no competitive pressures. This gentle approach absolutely excludes quick, strenuous movements that might cause trouble for the out-of-shape body. The key to correct performance — working slowly, carefully and with great concentration — is facilitated by breathing through the nose at all times. In other words, your pace when exercising is deliberate, never stressful, and you never feel any need to take in extra oxygen through your mouth. Always keep lips closed and teeth relaxed, as in Taking a Breather. As I have noted again and again, the *why* of doing these exercises is as important as how to do them. Exercise for your own sake, consciously choosing optimum health as your goal.

SUGGESTIONS

Wear loose clothing.

Exercise in a well-ventilated room or in a private outdoors place.

Never exercise on a full stomach.

Never eat until thirty minutes after exercising.

Practice daily four times a week or more, keeping to the same days and hours.

Sun Series

This series of twelve movements limbers you for the other exercises. I have found that these whole-body stretches make the body pliant and help release tensions. Once you have mastered them, do them in a continuous flow like a dance. Work on coordinating your breathing as indicated. Always breathe through the nose and exhale slowly.

1. Stand erect, arms alongside body, feet slightly parted. Bring your hands together in the prayer position close to the upper chest in salute to the god within and the energy that sustains you.

2. *Take a deep breath,* raise your arms overhead, upper arms touching ears, hands together high above head. Slowly bend backward. Arch your back with beautiful control. Read the ceiling overhead. With practice, one day you will be able to read the wall behind you.

3. *Exhale* bending forward. Grasp your ankles. Keep knees straight.
    Bring your face as close to your knees as possible.

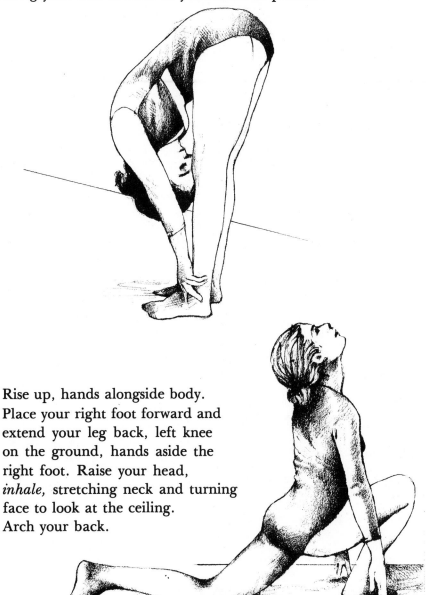

4. Rise up, hands alongside body.
    Place your right foot forward and
    extend your leg back, left knee
    on the ground, hands aside the
    right foot. Raise your head,
    inhale, stretching neck and turning
    face to look at the ceiling.
    Arch your back.

5. Without moving your hands *retain breath* and move right leg back keeping your body straight.

6. *Exhale* slowly as you place knees, chest and forehead on the ground, spreading hands and lowering upper arms. Keep buttocks slightly raised.

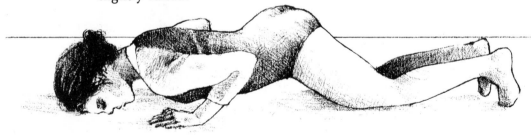

7. *Inhale* slowly, lowering knees and raise your head, arching your back. Keep your arms slightly bent and pubic arch firmly on the ground.

8. *Exhale* keeping your hands firmly placed, with toes on the ground, raise your buttocks up toward the wall behind you and press your heels down to the ground.

9. *Inhale* as you bring the left foot forward and extend your right leg back with right knee on the ground. Place hands beside your left foot, raise your head and look at the ceiling as you arch your back.

10. Stand up and bring both legs together. *Exhale,* as you bend down to clasp your ankles, face close to the knees as possible. Try not to bend your knees.

11. Rise and *inhale* as you bend back raising your arms overhead for a wonderful stretch.

12. *Exhale* and relax to original prayer position.

Do the twelve postures at least twice, working up to four, then six repetitions. Afterwards lie down, relax and breathe deeply.

For the Legs

The following movements should be done in the order indicated. At first do only as much as feels comfortable, but work until you are able to do them all with control and without strain. This series is excellent for firming the legs, thighs, and abdomen, and for releasing tension and keeping the body supple.

1. Lie flat on your back, arms stretched comfortably overhead. Throughout, remember when extending the leg to point your toes. Bring the right leg up slowly to the count of four until it is perpendicular to the body. Then down, counting slowly: 1, 2, 3, 4.
    Now the left leg up slowly to the count of four, and down.
    Bring both legs up: 1, 2, 3, 4, and down to the ground.

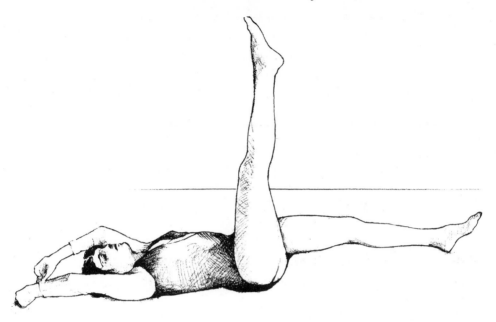

2. On your back, arms still stretched comfortably overhead, bring the right leg up perpendicular to the count of: 1, 2, 3, 4. Swing the leg down to the right side of your body, keep the knee straight and toes pointed.

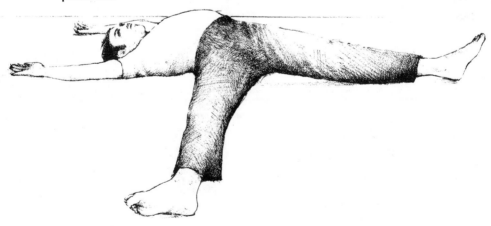

To the count of four again, lift the leg slowly.

Now swing it across and down to the left side of your body, with control, keep the knee straight: 1, 2, 3, 4.

Bring the leg up and back down to the ground in front of you.

Repeat the exercise with the left leg. Again to the count of four. Knees straight, toes pointed.

3.   Now repeat with both legs without a count. Keep legs together with toes pointed. Raise legs perpendicular and swing to the right side of the body. Up again and then swing to the left side of the body.

Straighten the legs up and then down slowly to the ground in front of you.

If you find this difficult at first you may stabilize yourself by extending your arms at shoulder level instead.

Remain flat for a minute and take several deep breaths.

4.   Still on your back, stretch arms overhead again. Lift both legs, pause, then stretch legs wide apart, and bring them together.

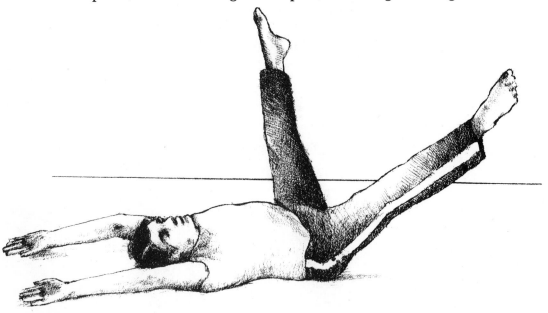

Again stretch your legs apart, this time bending your knees. Bring knees together and straighten your legs up again.

Keeping upper body and head on the ground reach up and try to take hold of your ankles. Keep your knees straight!

At first you might not reach the ankles; grasp the calves instead, but keep trying until you can eventually grasp the ankles. This creates a wonderful pull on the spine.

Holding the ankles, spread the legs wide apart and then together; apart again; and together.

Continue holding ankles and bring your knees toward your chest.

Lift your forehead up toward your knees and, with heels on buttocks, begin to rock in this position.

Rock forward and back two or three times.

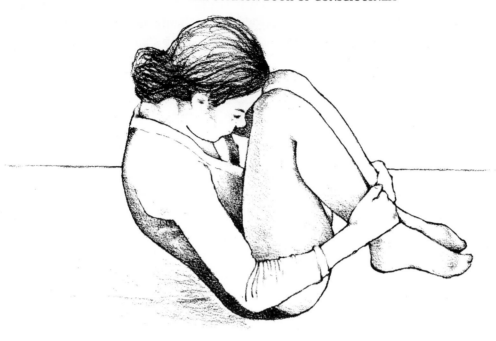

After rocking return your head to the ground. Keep a hold on your ankles and straighten legs again for one last great pull on your spine.

Release your ankles. To the count of four lower your legs and move your arms back to the original overhead position. Relax a moment.

Bring arms to your sides and take several calm breaths.

Rocking

This is fun and most beneficial to a flexible spinal column. It is particularly good for the blood circulation and, as such, I believe it combats aging. Most back problems arise from a stiffened, inflexible spinal column. Remember not to strain. Rocking should be done in a relaxed and masterful manner and become as important as brushing your teeth or combing your hair.

Sit on the floor and bring your knees to your chest. Clasp your hands together under your knees and rock back.

As you do, straighten your legs so that your feet touch the ground behind your head.

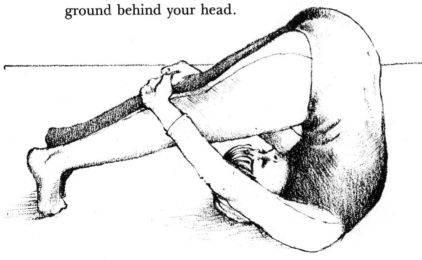

Rock back to the sitting position and repeat seven or eight times at the same speed.

At first you may not be able to move your legs over your head to touch the ground behind you; this will depend on your physical condition. Do not be discouraged. Bring your straightened legs as far back as possible. Work until you master this. The benefits are endless.

A Variation

Sit with your ankles crossed, take hold of your feet. Keeping your ankles crossed rock back and touch your toes on the ground behind your head. Do not straighten the legs.

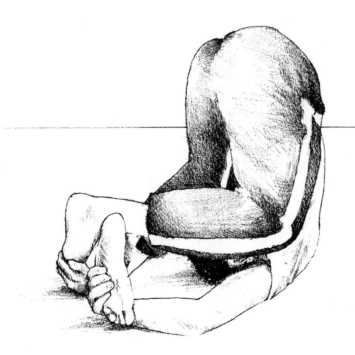

Keeping the position, rock back up and touch your forehead to the ground in front. Do this five times or more.

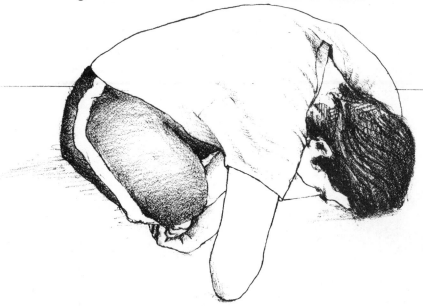

Now lie down and relax, legs and arms spread, eyes closed. Breathe through your nose, slowly drawing each breath from your stomach.

Headstand

The headstand is an advanced exercise that you should not attempt to complete while alone. I first tried the headstand in my mid-twenties, when working with Ida, my first yoga teacher. It was a great challenge and took weeks of practice before I could master it. Believe you can and eventually you too will master this difficult exercise. Take your time and practice parts one and two repeatedly and carefully before starting work on part three. Always have someone assisting as you learn. Do not strain or force yourself no matter how limber or strong you may be.

Aside from its excellent physical benefits, the headstand can be used as a posture for concentration as well. I have been told it has spiritual benefits.

Every stage of this exercise must be done step by step with perfect control and balance. The patience is as valuable as the act.

1. Kneel and sit back on your heels, knees and feet together, stomach and buttocks firm. Clasp your hands gently and place them on the ground in front of you making a triangle with your hands and elbows.

Place the top of the head into the cup of your hands. Straighten your legs, walk toward yourself until your buttocks are directly over your head. Pause and feel this position.

2. Carefully let your feet leave
    the ground, moving the
    weight of your body onto
    your head and hands.
    As you lift off bend your
    knees to your chest. Hold
    this position until you
    are balanced and in
    control.

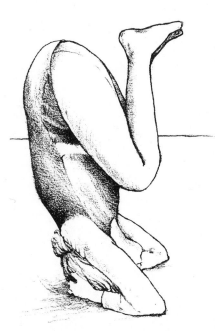

3.   Slowly extend your legs up, reaching for the sky.

Do not strain. Practice until you can remain three to five minutes. Remember it is important *how* you do this.

For further challenge do the following while in the headstand. Stretch your legs wide apart, then bring them together.

Bring right leg forward, left leg back. Then bring them together. Alternate, left leg forward, right leg back, and together.

Now bend your knees and cross your ankles. Slowly bring your knees down to your chest. Hold this position for five seconds.

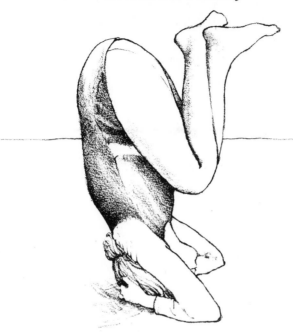

Calmly, straighten up, legs together with toes pointed right toward the ceiling.

When coming down from the headstand you must maintain control.

Bend your knees down first to your chest. Slowly come down and place your feet on the ground, moving the weight of your body onto feet.

Come onto your knees and lower buttocks to heels. Keep your head down on the ground for thirty seconds until the blood in your body equalizes. Stretch out on your back and relax. Close your eyes and congratulate yourself.

A Shoulder Stand

This simple exercise strengthens the back and stimulates blood flow in the head and upper body.

1. Lie down, arms at your sides, palms down, legs together. With your toes pointed, raise your legs while lifting your buttocks and hips up.

   Help keep the lower body erect and stable by using arms and hands to prop your back. Your chin will be resting on your chest. In this position your legs and trunk should be perpendicular. Stomach and hips should be aligned.

   Hold the stand as long as possible and breathe. Keeping the left leg straight up bring the right leg down to the ground over your head. Keep both knees straight. Pause, and then bring the left leg down. Slowly swing both legs up to the perpendicular position.

2. While still in the shoulder stand bring both legs down to the ground over your head. Point your toes and keep your knees straight.

Slowly bring your legs up to shoulder stand. Repeat this three times.

3.   While still in a shoulder stand with toes pointed directly toward the ceiling spread legs wide apart and bring both down over your head.

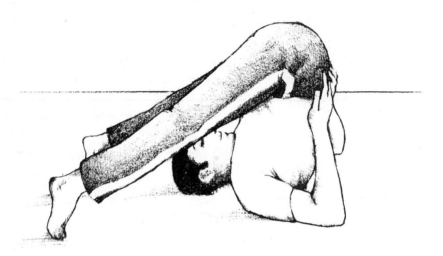

Return the right leg up first, then the left leg. Keep your knees straight! Now bring legs together.

4.   Using your hands and arms on the ground to help the transfer of your weight, lower your body, inch by inch, vertebra by vertebra. Keep your head on the ground.

    Turn your palms over; close your eyes and relax again while you breathe slowly.

A Half-Fish

This exercise is for stretching the neck, stimulating the thyroid, and bringing extra blood to the face. It is also good for the skin.

    Lie on your back, palms down and under your buttocks. Arch your back until the top of your head is on the ground.

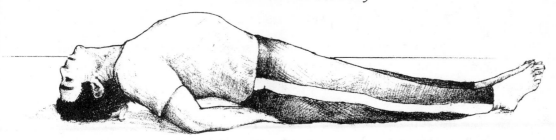

Now lift your right leg straight into the air. Next lift the left leg—toes should be pointed toward the ceiling.

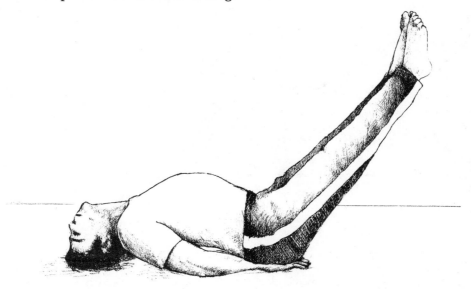

Lower both legs halfway to the ground; the slower you do this the better. Then lower them all the way down to the ground.

After a pause arch further back until the top of your head is on the ground. This stimulates the thyroid. Slowly relax back; release your hands. Relax and breathe.

The Plow

It would be best to attempt this exercise in stages. Remember not to bend your knees. It is important to take your time and keep your legs straight as you lift buttocks and hips off the ground.

1. Lie on your back, legs together, arms along your body, palms down. Keeping your legs straight lift them up over your head until your toes touch the ground behind you.

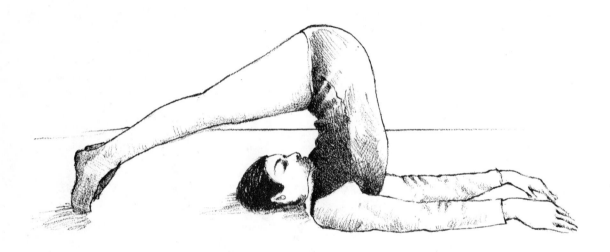

Straighten your knees for maximum benefit while you bring your legs over your head. Do this with balance and control. Try to touch your toes to the ground. This is the plow position; try to hold it for a count of ten.

2. Slowly raise both legs straight up in the air; then lower them, letting your toes touch the ground behind your head. Repeat.
    Reach back and take hold of your ankles and pull your legs wide apart; then move them together, and repeat.

Holding your ankles and keeping the legs straight, rock up into a sitting position and back down.

Bring your legs together with toes on the ground behind your head.

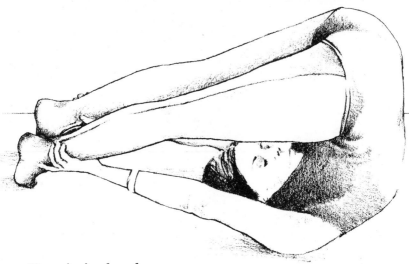

Remain in the plow.

3. From the plow, bend your knees and wrap your arms over the backs of your knees so the palms of your hands are on your ears.

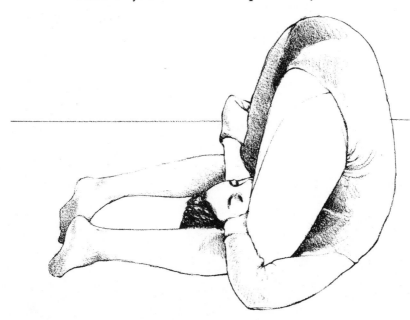

Take a deep inhalation and then exhale. Repeat. Remain in this position for at least ten seconds.

4. Return to the plow position and bring your arms back over your head parallel to your legs. Keeping your arms on the ground, begin to lower your body slowly, vertebra by vertebra. Inch your way down. Keep tightening the small of your back and your stomach muscles. Point your toes and keep your legs straight all of the way.

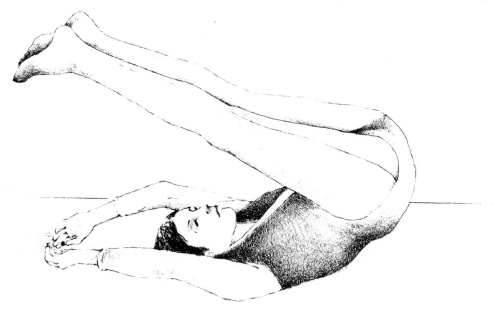

Try not to lose control as your buttocks get close to the ground. This part of the exercise is especially good for strengthening the back.

Relax with your arms still over your head and take a few deep breaths.

A Plow-Combination

1. Lie on your back, with your arms on the ground over your head. Begin to sit up, reaching for the sky.

Tuck in your stomach, bend further, and try to take hold of your ankles. Your elbows should be on the ground. Bend until your forehead touches your knees.

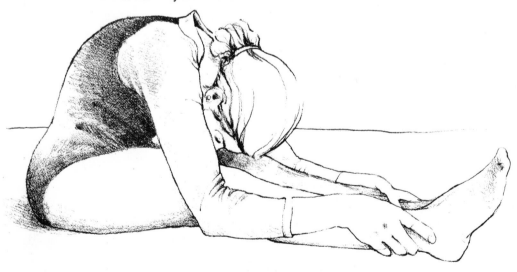

Move your stomach in and out several times as you inhale and exhale.

Release your ankles and slowly sit up, arms reaching for the sky. Counting, take thirty seconds to lie back down. Be aware of the muscles in your back. Try not to let your heels leave the ground.

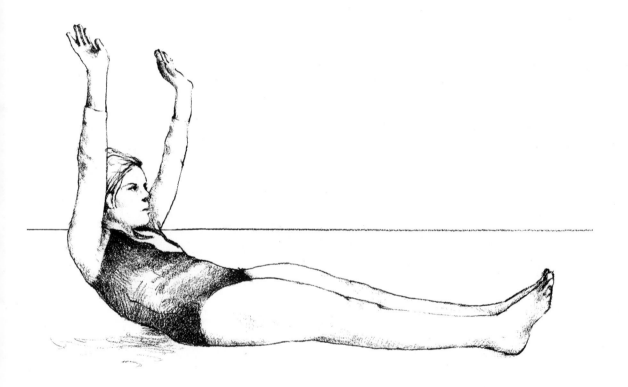

This is a fine exercise for balance and is wonderful for the stomach. Relax for a few seconds and breathe deeply.

2. Lying on your back with your arms on the ground over your head, resume the plow position in one smooth swing. Keep the knees straight!

First spread your legs wide apart above your head and then come down slowly, vertebra by vertebra. Point your toes to the wall behind. Keep your hands on the ground behind your head. Try to maintain control.

Relax for several deep breaths.

3.   Now sit up, with your legs spread in front of you. Reach for the sky and then bend forward placing your right hand on the right ankle, and your left hand on the left ankle. Bend as far as you can. Try to place your forehead on the ground.

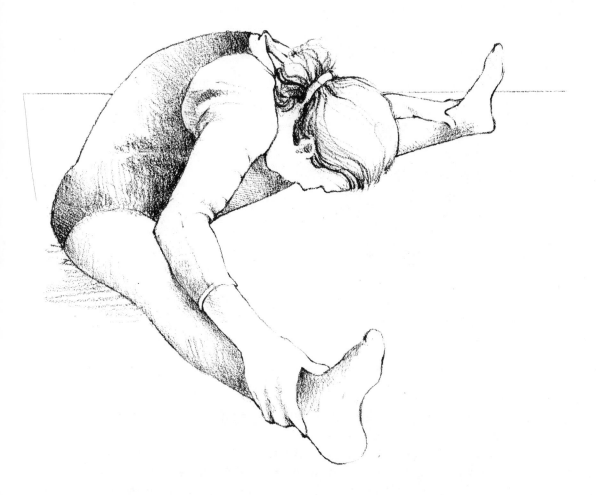

Sit up.

4. Remain sitting with your legs spread. Clasp both hands on your right ankle and bend foreward placing your forehead on your right knee.

Sit up.

Repeat for the left leg, with your hands on your left ankle, forehead on your left knee.

Sit up. Remember to keep knees straight.

Now move the right hand to the right toes and the left hand to the left toes; try again to bend down and place your forehead on the ground between your legs.

Sit up, bringing both legs together in front of you. Place your hands on the ground alongside your hips, with your palms down.

Raise your body straight up and drop your head back. Push your stomach up toward the ceiling.

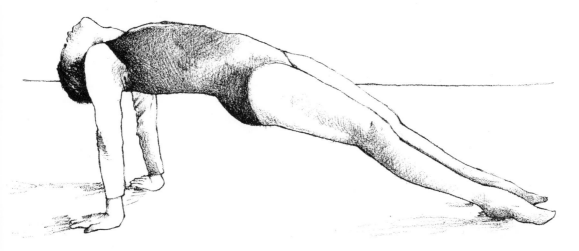

From this position raise your right leg up in the air, then down.

Now raise the left leg, up and down.

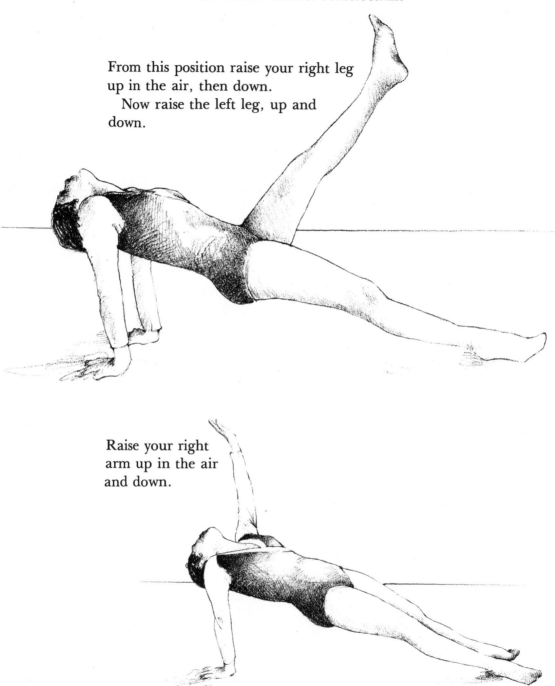

Raise your right arm up in the air and down.

Raise your left arm in the air, and down.

Slowly lie down and relax. Take sixty seconds of complete relaxation.

The Rise

Lie on your stomach, forehead on the ground, hands alongside your shoulders. Do this exercise to the count of nine.

Inhale slowly and raise your head to the count of 1, 2, 3 — now shoulders up to 4, 5, 6 — and begin to straighten your elbows, moving your face parallel to the ceiling with 7, 8, 9. Keep your pubic arch firmly on the ground as you arch the small of your back.

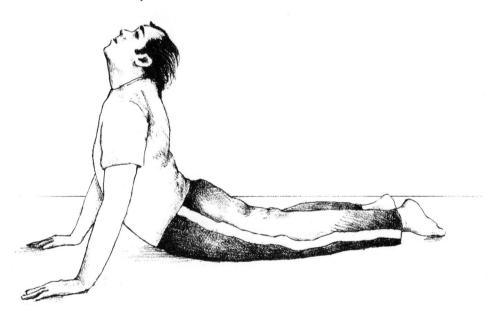

Exhale coming down — 1, 2, 3, 4, 5, 6, 7, and head down — 8, 9.

Do *not* bring your face down before the count of 7.

Repeat the exercise.

Cradle your head in your arms and relax.

For the Stomach

1.   Kneel with your knees apart, your back straight and the tops of your feet on the ground.

Squeeze your shoulder blades together.

Drop your head back.

Push your stomach forward and place hands on your heels. Hold to a count of four, then return to starting position.

The key to this exercise is squeezing the shoulder blades.

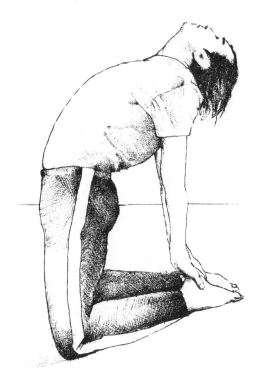

2.   Kneel with your knees apart.

Sit back, grasp your heels and bend forward placing the top of your head on the ground in front of you.

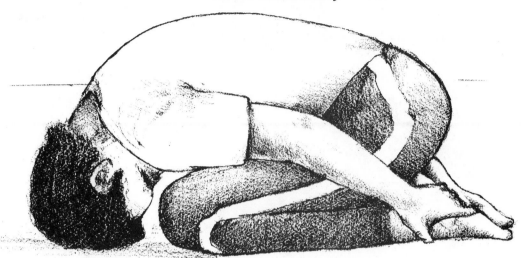

3. Rise to your knees and again squeeze the shoulder blades together. Drop your head back and grasp your ankles while you push your stomach forward.

4.   Rise to knees and sit back down on your heels. Grasp your heels as you lower your chin to the ground.

5.   Rise to knees and place your hands on your hips. Arch your back and courageously bend back. Try to put your head on the ground behind you. Use your elbows for support.

Work your way back down to the ground and cross your arms on your chest.

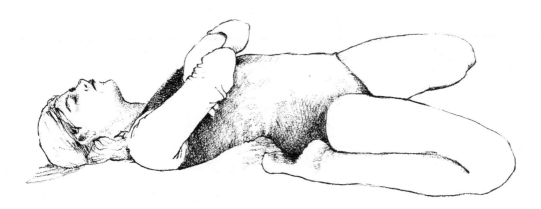

In this posture, inhale and exhale slowly. Now, be in control of your body, and rise to a sitting position. This is difficult at first, but you will master it if you keep trying.

Release arms and legs and lie down to rest.

Breathing

We seldom realize that breathing needs exercise. Most breathing we do is what is termed "clavicular," or shallow breathing, which tends to deny the body an optimum oxygen supply. Breath exercises correct this fault. They should be done daily, especially after completing an exercise sequence. They can be performed during a break at work. The benefits are priceless. You can reduce stress and energize your entire system. To improve the breath is to improve life. Breathing exercise is a device for improving your physical, mental and spiritual capacities. To gain the levels of awareness you seek, you should begin a regular practice of correct breathing.

Four breathing exercises follow. When practicing them, sit comfortably on a chair or sofa, or on the floor cross-legged, with your torso and head erect to insure maximum lung capacity. Relax and breathe in and out through your nose. Feel the air passing across the air passages behind your nostrils. Be aware of this subtle sensation. As you breathe in, expand your abdomen, diaphragm, and chest in that order. Reverse when exhaling. Imagine breath like a circle of air coming in and going out. Never force breath or make yourself rigid with air, and do not move your shoulders. Breathe naturally and feel your center. Feel the force of life entering your body, filling every cell and atom with energy. Be conscious of directing this new energy through breathing.

1. Sneezing and Clearing the Lungs

    Sit with back and head erect. (It might be advisable to keep tissues at hand.) Sneeze only through your nose. Each time you expel air snap in your stomach. Do forty fast expulsions.

    Inhale and count as you sneeze—1-2-3-4-5-6-7-8-9-10—all the way to 40!

    Pause, inhale deeply, and slowly exhale.

    Do fifteen sneezing explusions, but this time much slower and harder. Sneeze so that you can hear yourself.

    Inhale and count as you sneeze—1-2-3-4-5 through 15!

    Remember nothing should move except the stomach. Do not shake your shoulders.

    Inhale deeply and exhale and relax for twenty seconds as you breath becomes normal.

2. Changing Air

    In this exercise you exhale more than you inhale in order to clear dead air from the lungs.

    Inhale—1-2-3-4-5.

    Exhale—1-2-3-4-5-6-7-8-9-10.

    Repeat.

This time inhale to the count of ten and exhale to the count of twelve.

Inhale—1-2-3-4-5-6-7-8-9-10.

Exhale—1-2-3-4-5-6-7-8-9-10-11-12.

Relax and breathe normally.

3. Breath Retention

Sit erect and be comfortable and relaxed. Inhale slightly more deeply than normal but don't make yourself rigid with air. Practice will help. The important thing is not to force breath retention whereby you expel the air all at once.

Inhale—1-2-3-4-5—and hold for forty five seconds. Think of the good you do for yourself by bringing extra oxygen to the blood. This is good for the nerves and the skin. Feel yourself gaining extra strength.

Exhale—1-2-3-4-5-6-7-8-9-10.

Relax and breathe normally.

Try again, this time holding for sixty seconds.

Inhale—1-2-3-4-5.

For one minute visualize the pleasant day or evening ahead, the weekend to come. Great changes may take place. You may meet someone who will be important to you, perhaps do a small but great kindness. Find someone who has a need and fulfill that need. Feel strong and create a victory in this one minute.

Exhale—1-2-3-4-5-6-7-8-9-10.

Relax.

4. Alternate Nostril Breathing

I feel this is the best breath exercise. It is especially good for combating agitation or anger, nervousness, or insomnia. The more you do, the more you benefit. (It is important to notice the accumulative count.)

Make a fist of your right hand, extend the thumb and your two smaller fingers. Place the thumb to close the right nostril and inhale through the left nostril. Inhale—1-2-3-4-5.

Close both nostrils to retain breath—1-2-3-4-5.

Release the thumb and exhale through the right nostril—1-2-3-4-5.

Close the left nostril with your two smaller fingers and inhale through the right nostril—1-2-3-4-5-6.

Close both nostrils and retain the breath—1-2-3-4-5-6.

Release the left nostril and exhale—1-2-3-4-5-6.

Inhale through left nostril—1-2-3-to-7.

Close nostrils and retain breath—1-2-3-to-7.

Release the right nostril and exhale—1-2-3-to-7.

Inhale through right nostril—1-2-3-to-8.

Close nostrils and retain breath—1-2-3-to-8.

Release the left nostril and exhale—1-2-3-to-8.

Inhale through left nostril—1-2-3-to-9.

Close nostrils and retain breath—1-2-3-to 9.

Release the right nostril and exhale—1-2-3-to-9.

Inhale through right nostril—1-2-3-to-10.

Close nostrils and retain breath—1-2-3-4.

Release your fingers and exhale through your left nostril—1-2-3-to-10.

Inhale through left nostril — 1-2-3-to-10.

Close nostrils and retain breath — 1-2-3-4.

Release your fingers and exhale through right nostril — 1-2-3-to-10.

Inhale through right nostril — 1-2-3.

Close nostrils and retain breath — 1-2-3-4-5.

Release your fingers and exhale through left nostril — 1-2-3-4-5-6-7-8.

Inhale through left nostril — 1-2-3.
Close nostrils and retain breath — 1-2-3-4-5.

Release your thumb and exhale — 1-2-3-4-5-6-7-8.

This regimen is a wondrous, natural system that soothes and relaxes. You will feel the results immediately.

For the Eyes

Sit comfortably erect. Do not move your head or shoulders; move only the eyes.

1. Place your index finger at arm's length. Keeping your eyes focused on your finger, bring the finger forward until it touches your nose. Let your gaze follow your finger as you extend it at arm's length again. Repeat this in-and-out focus at least ten times.

2. Stare ahead. Lift your gaze to a spot on the ceiling directly above you; then look down to the ground in front of you. Look up at the ceiling again; then down. Repeat the motion ten times.

    Close your eyes for thirty seconds and breathe deeply.

3. Open your eyes. Snap your gaze to the far right and back to the far left. Repeat this sweep at least ten times.

4. Open your eyes and stare ahead. Now, as if following the circumference of a large circle, let your eyes begin from the bottom circling your gaze toward the right, up, around to the left and down. *Do not move your head.* Begin again at the bottom and circle to the left, rolling your eyes slowly up to right, and around.
   Repeat this exercise ten times.

   Gaze forward and gently place the palms of your hands over closed eyes. Breathe deeply.

   Later, as you get more proficient in these eye exercises you may wish to extend the number of repetitions.

Eye exercises strengthen eyes and may even halt the progressive deterioration of eyesight. Because of exercising the eyes, you may not need stronger glasses. Activating more rods and cones through the exercises results in wider, heightened vision.

For the Neck

Sit comfortably with your back erect, keeping your shoulders still. Nothing should move except your head.

1. Snap your face to the right—then forward. To the left—then forward. Repeat twice.
   Now tilt your head down to the right shoulder; then up. Tilt to your left, then up. Repeat this twice.
   After a pause, without moving your shoulders, extend the face and neck forward. (The movement is similar to the movement of a turtle's head.) Move your head backward and forward two or three times.

2. With your eyes closed, drop your chin to your chest and do some neck rolls. First roll your head to your right shoulder and back. Then roll it to the left shoulder, forward and down.
   Now to the left shoulder, back; then to the right shoulder, forward and down.
   Repeat the neck rolls two or three times.

3. While sitting on the ground, with your head erect and eyes open, lean forward and place your elbows on the ground with your hands cupping your face as you stare at the wall ahead. Feel the pull on your spinal column. Hold this position for thirty seconds.

   Sit up, and repeat.

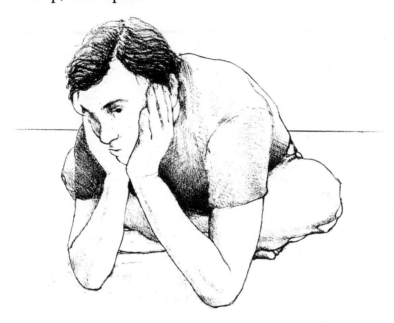

Now sit comfortably again and relax.

Going Within

Going Within, a variant of the yogic "corpse asana," is the ideal ending of any exercise sequence. I recommend it as the last step of any routine of physical activity—after jogging for example. Yet it can be done any place, anytime, exclusive of exercise. I find it marvelous before dinner or bed. As relaxation during a crisis it provides unbelievable benefits. Properly practiced it well might be as complete a means of relaxation as any devised. It transcends the physical: by relieving tension, calming muscles and the nervous systems, it melts the body away so that the mind is free to experience rare relief. It is a way of rearranging the senses and producing a you-essence from which renewed energy comes.

Some people use this exercise for meditation, but I feel this would take extensive practice. Nonetheless, Going Within brings a unification of selves —physical and emotional—which, once begun, will not easily be abandoned.

Ideally this exercise should be done for fifteen or twenty minutes, but thirty-fifty minute poses are not unusual. A flat, comfortable surface is necessary. The body must lie on a straight plane. A firm bed or soft carpet is best. I list this exercise last and it might be appropriate to shower and then return to finish the sequence by Going Within.

In any case, take several deep breaths before lying down. Rotate your arms and twist the trunk of your body as you stand. When you lie down on your back keep up the slightly exaggerated breathing as you spread your arms and legs. The palms of your hands should be up. Settle your head and shoulders so that your neck is in line with your spine. Relax your jaw muscles but keep your lips closed and, as always, breathe only through your nose.

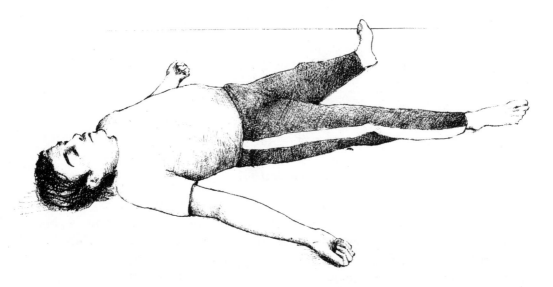

Close your eyes. Roll gently and adjust your arms and legs. They should be spread at the same angle from your torso. After practice the best angles will become apparent.

Check that no clothing binds you.

If possible, take off all your clothes and cover yourself with a light sheet.

Always be careful of drafts.

Suffer any itch or irritation. Once you have begun to Go Within do not move nor open your eyes. Begin to quiet the body. Let go. Let the stomach do the breathing. Slow the breath. After a while you will become familiar enough with the rhythms of your heart that you can slow them as well.

Allow the waves of tension to rise off. Continually release your hands and neck and face. This allowance can be made over and over again. One of the mysteries of Going Within is to discover the layers of tension within the body. After the basic technique is mastered it is sometimes disquieting to feel perfectly at ease and then be delicately shaken by even deeper relaxation.

Last, and most difficult, let go of the brain. Emergencies, responsibilities, errands, and important calls to be made will splash in your brain. Things to buy, laundry to be done, a letter to be written. . . a never-ending, multidimensional parade of petty urgencies will rain upon you. Ignore them!

With your thoughts follow the slow rise and fall of your stomach as it breathes. After a few minutes you can reduce that breathing. You can begin simple visualization: a diamond soaring into the distance. . . turning circles around each breath. . . thinking sinks, the brain becomes clear and begins to rest.

Once centered, never move.

Fall like a sleeping child, secure in the arms of the strong, the loved, the safe—sheltered from any thoughts that might intrude.

Once mastered this pose can be used for more sophisticated unification. It would be good for beginning experiments with the potential of out-of-the-body experience, or beneficial during a carefully planned fast. It can be a grounding for comprehending the early limits of altered states of consciousness. Guidelines for the latter are discussed in Chapter Five.

At first you may fall asleep. *Do.* You won't sleep too long—just enough to fill a need. As you come back from Going Within do so slowly, as you might return from a magical reverie. Let your mind dwell on a great white light. Imagine the coming hours and day. Look forward to reflecting love. Remain still. This is the finest act you can perform. Feel a desire to serve, to give and to learn.

Come back slowly.

Open your eyes carefully and stretch, sit up, and salute the god within you.

III

Only by regular practice of exercise can anyone begin to achieve a greater sense of the reality of her or his body. We need to be serious about exercise. The true reason we exercise is that we seek to bring a vast change to daily existence. Recent research into longevity proves there is no reason we cannot live well past the age of one hundred. We need to see that the headstand developed at the age of thirty-five should still be performed at age eighty. We harbor dangerous illusions with regard to our bodies. Most overweight people live under the illusion that they are "really not too heavy." A great number of people live under the dangerous illusion that their health is "generally good." Daily exercise gradually breaks through these veils of our physical reality. Daily exercise soon reveals that there are countless subtly different editions of the self that are seldom recognized or understood. They are tragically overlooked in the sweeping priorities of money, love, the pressures of caste, class, and neighborhood or the responsibility of a whole earth. In such collective confusion the person's psyche is split off, is even alienated, from its psychosomatic ground. The inherent integrity is violated, disorder and disease threaten the person's health. Carefully planned and faithfully executed exercise not only insures against this, it provides other benefits as well.

An important benefit for me was discovering how exercise combined with meditative practice became a powerful antidote to loneliness. It caused the kinds of change that occur in the sensible unification of awareness. Dealing with my loneliness, existentially acting against self-alienation, produced in me a new poise. Unifying awareness was a way to dissolve a core of loneliness that had affected me more than I realized. The new-found confidence was exhilarating. This is probably one of the reasons why so many millions of Americans are jogging. Getting into touch with one's physical body is a sure way to end up feeling good. The much-revered "runner's high" and all its gradations are self-generated elixirs of life. Combining the impetus this provides with an overall goal of unifying awareness is what Jack Schwarz calls "the path of action." Properly planned, it leads to true change.

Go easy. Remember not to strain or force yourself. If you are to alter the history of your body for the remainder of your life, there obviously is no hurry. Above all, be personally comfortable. You should pamper yourself with the time you have created to initiate the body, the mind and the place into revolutionary holistic longevity.

And do not stop.

This is only a beginning. An important test lies ahead in regulating consumption, for optimum health is created by diet as much as exercise. Our body-mind practice is refined by what we do not eat and what we refuse to absorb. Beyond that, a keen understanding of the benefits of meditation is required as well as seeing how lifestyles determine the quality of daily living.

CHAPTER THREE

The Lifetime Diet

Individuals have some inescapable responsibilities for the way they conduct their lives. Among them is learning something about nutrition.
Roger J. Williams

Each being has only one body, and he may choose to nourish that body with the foods that grow in the earth, or he may choose to have someone else harvest the earthy food, process it, add chemicals to it, preserve it, put it into a plastic bag, put that plastic bag into a box, call it new, tell us that it will taste good, and most incredibly, tell us that it is food that will sustain our bodies when we eat it.

Ellen Buchman Ewald
Recipes for a Small Planet

I

Regular exercise and improved breathing techniques will hone the health of the body and help to relieve the accumulated tensions of stress, but without keen attention paid to every area of consumption we are far from the aims of awareness. We are not only what we eat and drink as food but also what we breathe, what we see and hear and otherwise take into and process within ourselves. The entire range of consumption affects not only the body but the mind and spirit as well. The chapter of lifestyle considers how to identify and rid your environment of polluting or energy-sapping items of the non-food variety; in this chapter we consider food and eating habits.

In industrialized societies far removed from the earth and completely dependent on transportation and technology for food, the sad truth is that most people do not know how to eat properly, that is, to obtain the nutrients they require in the correct amounts and proportions. It is often confusing and difficult to understand the true importance of proper diet. Even the concerned person follows tastes, which usually have been grossly manipulated by food technology and advertising, and habitually eats too much food of poor nutritional quality. The overfed, undernourished body, like the sluggish body, is a constant drain on vital energy. Sooner or later that body must fall into dis-ease.

To free the body and mind in such a way as to aid in expanding consciousness we must begin to acquire an acute sense of what we consume. We need to learn what a sound diet is, and to awaken our individual "body wisdom" that intuits the body's needs. Acting on this information and on this sense, we will bring about lasting changes of increased well-being; we will become lighter, more energized, more responsive to life and more able to explore realms of other awareness. The changes will be relative at first, depending on the individual, but steady effort determines progress.

To begin, we must eliminate the concept of eating a certain way for a certain period of time before returning to the habits of consumption that caused trouble in the first place. This is the traditional idea of dieting. We need only note the ridiculously large number of plain and fancy diets, dietary aides, schemes and gimmicks in order to realize the futility of dieting in the old way. Much seems contradictory and serves to confuse rather than clarify. Fads abound. This or that meal plan becomes fashionable, is promoted by a well-known authority or chewed on television by a famous personality or an Olympic athlete. We sometimes devour the absurdity by eating only three grapefruits a day, or six hard-boiled eggs and half a head of lettuce, or nothing but lean red meat and Vichy water. Usually all we are trying to do is lose weight in order to correct a physical condition we know to be unhealthy. Yet we practice more illusions. For a certain period of time —the weekend crash diet, the 21-day/10 pounds-away—we eat only certain things in strictly limited amounts, counting calories and bravely trying to ignore hunger pangs. But when that period is over, sooner or later, we slide back again into habits that made us overweight in the first place. Yoyo-ing the body back and forth to the tune of the dietary experts is asinine—it insults the body's ability to regulate itself and it demeans your control of yourself.

There can be only one diet! A final, lifetime diet. The keys are to become knowledgeable about the *quality* of food you eat and to learn to *prepare* your own food.

A lifetime diet is a plan of food consumption and a pattern of eating habits that is to be followed for the rest of one's life. It is not something to be adopted until a certain amount of weight is lost or a certain level of health is obtained. It is a control of consumption that avoids the hypocrisy of traditional dieting and brings eating into a sensible range. As one gradually develops and settles into a lifetime diet the body becomes properly nourished and gradually finds its proper weight, which will usually be far less than one thought was normal.

> Make the transition into your own lifetime diet step by step. Be subtle. Never treat change lightly. It can be shocking if gone into rashly. Remember the sort of change you seek. Break old habits and formulate a new discipline. Proceed patiently, slowly and surely.

Becoming aware of your own food preferences and eating habits is a prerequisite for changing them. One good way to do this is to use a small notebook that fits easily into your purse or hip pocket in which to keep a record of everything you eat and drink each day. Do this for a few days running every month over the course of six months. Begin the six-month period once you have started the exercise practices outlined in the last chapter. You need not be concerned with exact measures of the quantity—approximations will suffice—and you need not be bothered looking up calorie counts. But try to record whether the food was commercially preserved—frozen or processed—or freshly prepared from natural products. With bread and crackers, note whether the flour was refined or whole grain. With dairy products, note whether the food was full fat or low fat. Do not forget to record between-meal snacks, whether it was a candy bar, a piece of fruit, potato chips with a drink before dinner, or a glass of milk at bedtime. Of course, when you eat a restaurant meal it is not always possible to find out the source of the food on your plate, but ask the person who serves you in a friendly manner and you will probably learn what you want to know.

At the end of this six-month period, when you have become established in the discipline of exercise and keeping the food diary to use as the basis of change, you are ready to institute your own lifetime diet. You will see the value of limiting what you eat for the rest of your life. You will see the satisfactions than can be gained. The transition might require many months before it is complete. Challenge but do not deprive yourself. Keep on steadily toward your goal. In the eyes of some family members and friends you might begin to seem odd, but ignore the negative reactions of others. After all, your health and well-being is *your* responsibility. Follow the guidelines provided. A lifetime diet is not a fad; it need not restrict or confine you to rigid consumption. Rather it will impart discrimination to your eating habits. As the exercises put you in touch with the solid, physical reality of your body, new patterns of consumption will begin to put you in touch with the quality of your energy. Your intuition concerning your body's needs will awaken and the process of refining self-awareness will gain momentum.

This process has actually begun once we acknowledge that what and how much we eat makes the difference between burdening or releasing the self, between staying in the darkness of procrastination or rising naturally into the light of awareness. "You are what you eat" extends to what you see and hear. It extends to what you do and to what you desire. Greater awareness can start with a simple appreciation of the value of fresh food as compared with junk or instant nonfoods, which eventually should be eliminated. Expanding such awareness can make the difference between a second half of life lost in senility or one spent in vibrant health and with the capacity for using wisdom, age, and experience.

Do not hesitate. Heed your best instincts and resolve now to fulfill your desire for sane consumption. By thirty or forty years of age it becomes progressively harder to change long-standing habits. In the later years, at sixty or sixty-five, it becomes very difficult indeed.

etween the fresh, natural, whole food and its refined, fractioned commercial product there is an abyss of lost nourishment, even when the refined food has been enriched. In whole foods there is a balance between calories and other nutrients, a certain density of nourishment that is lacking in many refined foods. The basic requirements of human nutrition are water, carbohydrate, protein, a broad range of vitamins and minerals, and a little fat or oil. Whole foods contribute to many of these needs at once; refined foods often contribute to only one or two.

> Laurel Robertson, Carol Flinders
> and Bronwen Godfrey
> Laurel's Kitchen

My own final diet began unobtrusively several years ago. It rose out of hunger for fresh foods. Like most people who live alone, I had succumbed to the temptations of "easy foods." Convenience foods were so varied and handy that I lost incentive to prepare my own meals. It was so much easier to reach into the freezer compartment of the local supermarket and pick out a meal from a wide choice of frozen and prepared dishes. In addition to prepared dinners, I often cooked frozen meats. All I had to do was unwrap a steak for the broiler and make an effort at a salad. I could believe I was treating myself to a nutritious meal, one that was not packaged. The salad usually consisted of a handful of lettuce, maybe a tomato, and bottled dressing. Part of the lettuce always had to be thrown out because it had been refrigerated too long.

I had already begun to travel a lot in those days and my eating habits reflected this. Every now and then I realized that I was making an uneasy compromise. Thinking myself too busy to shop daily for fresh foods as my mother had done, yet not wanting to be wasteful, I stuck with frozen meals and packaged and canned goods. Often my energy was low yet I blamed this on jet lag, a hazard of my work. However, other doubts nagged at me. Sometimes after finishing a meal I suspected I had cheated myself.

Like most of my generation I grew up in a household that had never seen a TV-dinner or a frozen steak. My mother went to the market daily (or sent me!) to purchase fresh vegetables, fish or fruits. Beef at the time was an unusual treat. I was brought up on fish and, occasionally, a lamb dish. It was those meals I instinctively missed later, the wholesomeness of fresh food freshly prepared. I began to change my habit of convenience eating. I began by putting more effort into the preparation of meals even though it meant more trips to the market and more time in the kitchen.

For a long while this was an off-and-on-again thing that could have not been considered a new pattern of living. It was always dependent upon whether or not I had the time. Other priorities were resistant to change. I felt my newly forming eating habits were important but time was precious and hours were crammed with work and social activity. With the benefit of hindsight I can say that too much attention was given to relationships and faddish events that proved superficial. To use a metaphor from Sufism, I was frittering away my life as a counterfeiter among other counterfeiters, hardly aware at all of genuine value. Too much time was spent in seeking companionship. I rarely allowed myself to be alone. It was not until many years later that I realized that I feared loneliness and for this reason sought the company of a certain friend or special situation. Now I know full well that the friend I needed lives within and the fulfilling situation is a feeling of wholeness in myself.

Back then, however, I had no idea how a change of food and eating habits could lead to other changes that would profoundly alter the way I lived and who I was. All I knew was that I hungered for fresh, unadulterated, unrefined foods that would truly nurture me. And what I learned over a period of many years I have distilled here as the guidelines of a lifetime diet.

A word of caution: some people have medical disorders that call for special diets. The lifetime diet might require adjustment for many such people or it may not concern them at all. As always, anyone with a medical condition ought to check with his or her doctor before undertaking a change in diet. However, for the average person without clinical problems, a sweeping change in food consumption in accordance with the guidelines offered here, can be wholly beneficial to the creation or maintenance of a healthy body.

Let us start with what should *not* be consumed.

> All sugar and refined-flour products should be totally elimi-
> nated. Do not be misled by the product called "raw sugar," or the
> coarse brown sugar that sells at a premium price in many health-
> food stores. This stuff may be white sugar colored with a bit of
> molasses. White flour and white, or polished, rice are low-quality
> foods that have been stripped of most of their nutritional value
> and, apart from the quickly accessible fuel they provide, can only
> add weight to your body.

I discovered the facts about sugar in *Sugar Blues,* a fascinating work by William Dufty. Although sugar is made from a natural source, 90 percent of the cane or beet is discarded during processing. What remains is a highly acidic, completely nonnutritive chemical molecule. Sugar use is addicting. Sugar rapidly enters the bloodstream and provides instant energy spurts that fizzle out as quickly as they come. Meanwhile, the sugar dose has lashed the adrenal and pancreatic glands into emergency action and whiplash effects are experienced all around the endocrine system. Dufty quotes endocrinologist J.W. Tintera on the unequivocably good results of a sugar-free diet: "It it quite possible to improve your personality for the better. The way to do it is to avoid cane and beet sugar in all its forms and guises." It is imperative to remember too that sugar is the major cause of tooth decay and a prime agent in fostering obesity. Yet it is also important to recognize that a sweet dessert might be acceptable if the moment or the company were right.

White flour and white rice are not in the same zero-nutrition category as sugar, but these foods have had the best part of their nourishment refined away. Generations upon generations of Europeans and Asians have used whole wheat and unpolished rice as staples of their diet. In their whole, unrefined state, these are high-quality foods; processed and devitalized, they mainly supply fuel and much ends up on your hips, thighs and belly as excess weight.

Ridding your diet of sugar, white rice and white-flour products such as breads, rolls, pastries and pasta, may be difficult at first if you are not familiar with the alternatives.

Unfiltered honey can be used as a sweetener, but always in moderation. The body has absolutely no need for sweets. The desire or craving for sweetness is an acquired taste that you ought to shed as quickly as you can. Eat fresh fruit for dessert. Or end a meal with an herbal tea sweetened, if you must, with half a teaspoon of honey. Eat only brown or unpolished rice, which still has its nutrients. The French call it *riz complet,* and so it is: a complete food. Instead of foods made of white flour, choose those made from any whole-grain flour that has been stone ground, such as whole wheat or rye or Roman Meal. In addition to their nourishment, whole grains also provide the fibrous roughage that facilitates your natural elimination processes.

Drastically cut back on the amount of fat you eat. This includes the butter or margarine on your bread as well as oil used in cooking and the fats found in dairy products and meat—even the leanest cuts.

Nutritionists believe that the body requires certain essential fatty acids but they do not say how much, or how little, fat in the diet is necessary to meet these requirements. In *Diet and Nutrition* Dr. Rudolph Ballentine tells about a study made in India of a group whose total daily intake of fat per person was *less than a teaspoon* and who "presented no signs or symptoms which could be attributed to fat deficiency." The average American diet contains up to twenty times this amount of fat and one can say that we Americans present many signs and symptoms of excessive fat consumption by pointing to the great number of overweight and obese people, the high incidence of hardening of the arteries (even among youngsters and young adults), and the appalling cancer toll. Dr. Ballentine writes that the evidence is mounting that excess fat intake may be one of the major causes of cancer. The association "is well-documented in the case of cancer of the colon but may also be true in breast cancer as well." There is hardly any need to bring up the great bugaboos of heart disease and cancer in this context.

Unless you have been living on another planet until quite recently you well know that fat in your diet makes for fat on your body and that this is an unhealthy state of affairs. Perhaps you do not know, however, that close to half the total fat in the average American diet comes from meat. For this reason alone, you might well consider immediately cutting down by half or more your usual consumption of meat. However you accomplish it, a lifetime diet calls for a major reduction in the amount of fat that you consume.

> Eliminate all processed and canned foods (except some canned fish). This should include all obvious convenience items as well as the expensive "gourmet" goods. Sugar—also called dextrose, sucrose and cane syrup—is loaded into processed food as are dozens of chemical additives in order to make it pack and ship better, and to give it a long "shelf life," not to preserve its nutritional value.

Above all, read labels! Consumer groups have fought for and reasserted your right to know exactly what you are getting when you buy prepared foods. Many packaged and canned items are of dubious nutritional value even though they may taste good and look appealing to people who have forgotten or never known the taste and appearance of natural foods. The manufacturers of processed food spend millions of dollars on advertising to convince you that their products are good food. But slick color photos and the word-magic of Madison Avenue do not nurture; what nurtures are the natural constituents of unadulterated whole foods.

Another item very prominent in processed and canned foods is salt and other sodium compounds. Salt is the single greatest cause of high blood pressure, according to heart specialist Lot Page, and it is estimated that up to twenty-five million Americans suffer from this disease, many without knowing it. Worse, it seems that hypertensives crave salt, and it is known that salt, like sugar, is an addicting substance—the more one gets the more one wants. Dr. Page recommends less than a quarter teaspoon of salt a day. That is about one gram of salt. A large pickle contains two grams of sodium; two ounces of processed cheese nearly one gram. Sodium is plentiful in dairy products, fish and meat. The point is, you can easily get all the sodium your body needs without ever salting your food, and the excessive amounts of sodium they contain is another compelling reason to avoid all processed and canned products.

Instead of salt, I use herbs to enhance the natural flavor and taste of the foods I prepare. I also use Vega-Salt, a seasoning which has been in health-food stores for years. A seasoning guide is included on page 98. I experiment more with garlic, a hearty and healthful food about which songs have been sung and books written! Small amounts go a long way. Slice or crush the cloves and cook slowly in vegetable oil or butter. Be careful not to burn. Strain the liquid and use it to flavor cooked green vegetables. I also enjoy finely chopped fresh parsley or chives sprinkled on soups and salads just before serving. A few drops of fresh lemon juice add zest to all fish and poultry dishes and does wonders for green vegetables too.

The alternative to eating foods processed by profit-making industries is, of course, to prepare your own food. Yes, it takes more time and energy to do this than to slide a frozen TV-dinner into the oven but, to put it bluntly, if eating properly adds ten or twenty good years to your life, how foolish it is to "save" an hour or so a day by eating convenience foods. Still there is an even better reason. Shopping and cooking for yourself and your family will not seem such a tedious chore once you fully realize that those food-stuffs, lovingly and skillfully handled and prepared by you, literally become part of you and those with whom you share them. There is a joy in establishing communion with your food, and the pleasure in preparing wholesome meals arises from your awareness of nurturing the health and purity of yourself and the others with whom you share your life. The effort you make, the care you bring to this preparation, can be an act of love, an act that provides a vital ingredient that not only enhances the meal but brings intangible aid to the well-being of those with whom you share your food.

Preparing your own food will change the nature of the kitchen. Let the kitchen cheerfully reflect the vital changes you are making. A small area rug or two can be added. You can replace utility chairs with comfortable, wooden ones. Use pictures, posters, glass cannisters, and more colors. Try adding green plants, fresh and dried flowers, wooden cheese boards, wicker baskets for your fruits and vegetables. You can grow your own herbs along a window sill, your own sprouts on a counter top. The kitchen will become a more meaningful place, a place where food is a celebration.

And she had never forgot-
*ten that, if you drink much from a bottle marked
'poison,' it is almost certain to disagree with you, sooner
or later."*

Alice in Wonderland

I have said that one key to a lifetime diet is to become knowledgeable about the quality of foods, that is, their nutritional value. I do not mean to suggest by this that you need to study texts on the subject; on the other hand, you *are* obliged to inform yourself about fundamentals. A beginning has been made in the preceding section. Ridding your diet of empty calories and poor-quality food items puts you on the right road. Generally speaking, high-quality foods are those that combine into meals that supply complete protein, vitamins, minerals and essential fats along with their carbohydrates.

Daily eat plenty of fresh vegetables, raw in salads or lightly cooked. Eat raw and dried fruits and fresh sprouts such as mung bean and alfalfa. Eat hearty dishes containing whole grains and legumes such as beans, peas and lentils in combination. Eat seeds such as sunflower and unhulled sesame. Enjoy nuts and nut butters in moderation. A dish containing fish, poultry, eggs, or a dairy food such as milk, cheese and yogurt (with most of the butter fat removed) may be consumed once a day at first. Later you

> may wish to eat these latter foods less often, perhaps three or four times a week. It might be well to break the habit of drinking excessive or daily amounts of milk.

Another word can be said about meat. Many people believe that it is wrong to butcher mammals and eat their flesh. Others contend that meat contains potentially toxic additives that packers and processors use to "improve" its qualities. Whether these allegations are true or not, I do not recommend eating meat daily. I believe meat, especially beef, is a digestive burden. As noted earlier, it is important to cut back on fat consumption and fat is contained in even the leanest cuts. The fact that meat is notoriously expensive ought not to be overlooked either. Perhaps the best reason is that as a food, for those interested in alert life and good health, meat is simply unnecessary. Complete protein such as it provides is readily available elsewhere, and once removed from consumption it becomes easier to maintain lighter eating habits.

I found that as my eating habits changed my body did not need meat. I was learning to get excellent protein from fish, eggs, cheese and yogurt and combinations of grains and legumes. Meat was heavy and too much energy seemed wasted on digestion. Once I quit eating meat I was unable to eat it; it had an unpleasant taste. Whether or not you choose to exclude meat from your own lifetime diet, I urge you in the begining to cut back the amount you consume. Try a few days, or better yet, two or three successive weeks without it and be aware of the difference this makes in how you and your body feels.

In this context, there are two excellent books that I commend to your attention. One is *Diet for a Small Planet* by Frances Moore Lappé, and the other is *Recipes for a Small Planet* by Ellen Buchman Ewald. Ms. Lappé explains and gives examples of the concept of protein complementarity, which is "the combination, in proper proportions, of non-meat foods that produces high-grade protein nutrition equivalent to—or better than—meat proteins." She makes clear that plant protein is in no way inferior to animal protein, and that plant foods are superior to meat by virtue of the vitamins and minerals they contain and their virtual absence of fat. For example, a dish combining one-and-one-half cups of beans or peas with four cups of brown rice contains usable protein equivalent to nineteen ounces of steak. The tastiness and savoriness of such dishes is enhanced by the herbs and vegetables included. Ms. Lappé's work on protein complementarity was inspired by Ewald and grew into *Recipes for a Small Planet,* which contains hundreds of easy recipes that combine grains, legumes, seeds and dairy products into dishes that contain complete proteins as well as abundant vitamins and minerals. These books are fairly recent (published by Ballantine Books in 1971 and 1973, respectively), and both are available in an inexpensive paperback format.

II

Vary the foods you eat. This is a familiar principle of a sound diet, yet it bears repeating because people often seem to get stuck on a small number of favorite habits and dishes. Potatoes are a wonderful food; they can be prepared in countless ways. Instead of eating potatoes four or five times a week, however, try the tuber called Jerusalem artichoke, which is rather similar in texture but deliciously different in taste. Or enjoy sopping up the juices of your entree with fresh, hot, whole-grain biscuits, or egg noodles made with pastry-grade whole-wheat flour. Avoid fried potatoes, especially French fried, which involves deep-fat cooking. Cook potatoes, skins and all, after you have scrubbed them thoroughly; the skins themselves contain valuable nutrients. Diversifying your diet is important. Nutritionists know that the body requires more than forty different nutrients to sustain a high level of health. It is reasonable to expect that the more varied your choice of whole foods, the greater is the likelihood that these vital nutrients will be obtained.

Drink water, lots of water, each day. Drink vegetable and fruit juices for variety and herbal teas for refreshment and to complement your meals.

Experts say that one should drink eight glasses or two quarts of water per day. I like to get some of this amount mixed half and half with a fruit or vegetable juice. If you have any doubts about the purity of your tap water, investigate purification devices and meanwhile, buy natural spring water and use it in cooking as well as in the preparation of tea. As for other liquids available in the marketplace these days, avoid soft drinks of all kinds! I feel most carbonated drinks ought to be labeled with a skull and crossbones. Between the sugar or sugar substitute, the sodium, the coal-tar dyes and all the other highly distasteful additives, these concoctions might be useful as drain-cleaners and rust removers, but they are absolutely unfit for human consumption. Of alcoholic drinks, a lifetime diet should allow only occasional wine and beer. In moderate amounts, alcohol can be a beneficial addition to any lifetime diet.

As your consumption changes you should be alert to your changing tastes. If you are like me, coffee will begin to taste thick, oily, and acidic. After learning of the effects of the caffeine in coffee and tannic acid in fermented teas, and after some experimentation with alternatives I quit using both. I recommend herbal teas—the lighter in color the better—served occasionally with honey. The variety in herbal teas is wonderful:

Spearmint	Red Clover
Chamomile	Golden Seal Herb
Licorice	(Hydrastis Canadensis)
Alfalfa	Rose Hips
European Nettles	Fennel Seed
Lemon Grass	Sage
Indian Papaya Leaves	Comfrey Leaf
Winterberry	Peppermint Leaf
Matte Chicory	Matte

There are many herbal tea blends under different brand names. Once the taste of herbal tea is acquired, one becomes averse to the harsh, stronger taste of other liquids. Drinking of herbal tea is not only refreshing but soothing. The magic healing quality in herbs is a gift of nature that often tends to be ignored.

The other key to the lifetime diet is to prepare food yourself. The selection and preparation of what you eat is as important as the foodstuff. Preparation provides time in each day in which you think about and handle what you put into your body. Mind and hand participate in combining foods into appealing and wholly satisfying dishes. In working with foods, something of you goes into them and their nourishment is enhanced by your attentiveness. Food is life, and through awareness you treat life with new respect.

Remember—cook foods only as much as needed for complete digestion. Learn to use the wok. When stir-frying cut vegetables to bite-size. A pressure cooker is best for cooking whole grains. The multi-purpose juicer and food mill is a must for preparing fresh vegetables, fruit juices, and grinding grains into meals and flour.

Personally, over a period of years, I lean more and more toward vegetarianism because I love the lightness of fruits and vegetables and my body has lost the heavy habit of food. When I can manage it—as it needs about three or four hours—baking breads, rolls, and crackers of various whole grains provides immense satisfaction. It is simple to freeze half of the dough for the next time fresh-baked goods are desired. I do the same with other dishes that lend themselves to freezing, preparing twice as much as we need and freezing the rest for a meal the following week. Economy and efficiency are realized in this way, and proper storage and timely defrosting insures that little or nothing is lost of nourishment and taste.

Seasoning Guide

Poultry — Bay leaves, curry, ginger, marjoram, oregano, rosemary, sage, saffron, savory, tarragon, thyme.

Fish — Allspice, bay leaves, celery seed, curry, marjoram, mustard, oregano, sage, savory, tarragon, thyme.

Shellfish — Basil, bay leaves, chili powder, curry marjoram.

Cheese — Caraway seed, cumin, ginger, mace, mustard, oregano, rosemary, sage.

Somewhere in the conflicting impulses and urges that arise into our awareness when we think of eating is the data which we need to guide us to the food that our bodies require. These internal indicators have to be patiently retrained, however. What is often referred to as hunger, for example, is not really hunger at all but the socially or psychologically conditioned urge to eat. One has to filter out all the other connections involved with food, tuning in to the correct signals and tuning out the static.

Rudolph Ballentine, M.D.
Diet and Nutrition

II

These considerations lead us to a second major area of diet: eating habits and how much to eat. In America, generally speaking, our lives are plagued by an overindulgence in food. The reasons for doing so are numerous, overlapping and often unconscious, but the main reason is that feeling "full" is imagined relief from practically everything that ails us. Eating often becomes an act of aggression, an attack on boredom or frustration that gets repeated again and again with horrible results. Morever, snacking is a national tradition heavily promoted by television advertising that pushes junk food and drink with the vile insistence on the great fun of what is collective gluttony.

Chances are that the average person reading this book might cut out twenty, even thirty percent of what is eaten and not only furnish the body with enough nutrients but also restore a zestful appetite. To develop a sense of what and what not to eat, and how much to eat, one has to step back and then step back again to gain a perspective. Only then will we see the practicality of a basic principle of one's lifetime diet—when in doubt, don't! Don't snack. Don't indulge. Never fear to skip a meal. Eat wisely at regular mealtimes and begin to free the self from the dominations of consumption.

Freedom from old consumption habits furnishes a new command. If one's health is basically good and diet consists of wholesome foods and balanced meals, there is nothing nutritionally unsound about an adult eating but two, even one meal a day, or restricting consumption to fourteen to sixteen meals a week with three to five days of fasting every month. The benefits of regular, sensible fasting are incredible. Fasting relieves and stills the digestive system and provides a lightness of body and spirit too few people allow themselves to experience. The tyranny of food consumption is a wall against awareness. The average person's eating habits were formed under a commercial totalitarianism that actually impedes the development and maintenance of a truly healthy body and blocks the freedom of the real or imagined movement of that body.

We have made fetishes out of expedience and convenience. Consider the advertisements for fast-food chains, for sugared breakfast cereals, unnatural "orange juices." Consider the insidious insistence that to constantly drink milk is good for you. Many health experts feel this is quite untrue. Reconsider the ritualistic call for the consumption of "three squares a day!" Compare this to the glossy, grossly expensive commercials that inevitably follow homey skits extolling antacids and other stomach remedies—genteel pitches aimed at "hemorrhoid sufferers" and those "with occasional irregularity." Considering the tremendous cost of such advertising would seem to admit to a national constipation. Match these considerations with the pleasantly patriotic—idiotic—gluing and cleaning of dentures. Mindless vignettes which have become the treasure of prime-time television. Were it not sad, it would be hilarious that millions of people are so manipulated into false mystiques of overeating and wrongful eating, then sold products to undo the criminal mischief.

Since there is no money to be made from it, a conspiracy of silence seems to reign over the subject of sensible eating and the development of fasting habits. Having no one and nothing to support such a project, even people who know better shamelessly procrastinate.

"I can't fast because I'm too uptight."

"I could lose weight any time, if I wanted to."

Endless statements such as these ring false and fail to admit the addictive element of food. Overweight America is an international scandal. We seem obsessed with gorging ourselves and are constantly anxious about cleaning and eliminating the harried systems of our bodies that process what we eat. Does one eat to live or live to eat? Life priorities are confused if one spends too much time and energy on food. This confusion numbs the senses and anesthetizes the mind, keeping us from coping with the real problems and true challenges of human existence. Overeating and all its paraphernalia are thieves of health. Overeating and attendant problems are an insidious preoccupation of the body and mind that leaves no time or energy to think of freeing ourselves. We need to see that there is a greater reality in being free.

Fasting is an excellent tool.

Fasting is a way to cleanse the body's digestive and elimination systems and to purify all the senses. We shall begin to see it as a means of unburdening the body in such a way as to allow us a greater awareness. Fasting can bring us back to ourselves, so that we are better able to contemplate and act on the changes we instinctively desire.

Fasting cannot be taken lightly. It should be treated religiously. It is best to begin with an eight- or ten-hour fast during the day. For example, only two meals, perhaps abstaining from lunch and breaking the fast with a light meal toward evening. Or you may wish to abstain from breakfast and have one midday meal. *Do whatever is easiest.* Work up to the point where you eat only one meal, settling for juice or water for the others. Go gradually until your body becomes acclimated to the changes. Never push your body or shock it into a long fast. Always prepare. Always relax. The fast is a treatment for the mind as well as the body.

When you feel ready to fast for a 24- or 36-hour period try to be alone and remain quiet. Enjoy a day of silence. Conversation zaps energy. Some people might understand and respect the time you are devoting to yourself, but do not risk interruption. Free yourself from the telephone by unplugging it or putting it in a drawer under a pillow. Treat yourself to calm and relaxation. By fasting you are caring for yourself by purifying your body and training yourself to eat less. Allow the quiet and reverie. Play soothing music or spend time reading. Write or paint or even dance flowing with the music, letting your body move in the rhythm of a dance of its own. Do nothing laborious. Focus on yourself and the changes you may feel in your body. Your senses will be heightened and, after the hunger pangs have receded—and they always do recede—you will experience a new clarity that will beckon you again and again.

When you break a fast do it with gentle control. Eat lightly, a nourishing soup or a melon, apple or pear. Later, you may have a meal, but be aware of how much your stomach has shrunk. Above all, watch what you eat. Chew slowly and eat less. As you come off a fast dwell on the matter of nutrition and consumption. You will be lighter, more energetic, and more ready to feel. You will have escaped the intoxication of food and the lethargy. You will have begun to escape the tyrannies.

At the beginning of this chapter I used the phrase "body wisdom" and spoke of the need to intuit the body's nutritional requirements. Although this seems to be a somewhat mysterious faculty, people versed in scientific knowledge about nutrition do refer to it. Thus, the eminent biochemist Roger J. Williams has written that "one of the regulatory mechanisms or 'wisdoms' of the body is that we eat when we are hungry and stop when we have had enough. . . . It seems probable that individual nutritional needs are met to a degree by the self-selection of foods. This is particularly so when the selection involves only wholesome foods. . ." Williams, Rudolph Ballentine and my late grandmother agree, however, that for most people in America today this intuition has been numbed by years of wrongful eating habits drilled into place from early infancy by commercial interests and abetted by the natural perversity of human nature. We confuse what we hunger for with what we desire to eat and, as a consequence, the body does not get what it needs. It is fed what we want. The guidelines of a lifetime diet point the way out of this tyranny. *A lifetime diet should be incorpo-*

rated systematically, slowly and thoughtfully. Bearing in mind that these are guidelines only and not a detailed set of instructions, use them to inspire your personal investigations of your individual nutritional requirements. As you gradually progress in learning the truth about foods and apply the learning, you can expect to hear from and be aided by the intuitive wisdom of your body. The careful and considered use of the tool of fasting is the key help along the way.

Sensible eating concerns what and how much and also the manner in which food is eaten. Many people habitually hurry through their meals. If there is not enough time to sit down and eat at a pace that respects both the food and the diner, I suggest that the time is better spent not eating at all. A short walk or a brief meditation would be healthier. Even when there is time to enjoy a meal leisurely, many tend to hurry. The development of slower eating habits is imperative. Not only is it beneficial to the digestion but thorough chewing slows down the food intake and allows you the opportunity to taste and relish the meal. By this means alone it is possible to eat less without feeling a sense of deprivation.

A calm atmosphere should reign over your dining area. Mealtime should be a period of appreciation, praise, and gratitude for the food that sustains our life and the people who have brought the food to our table. The radio and the stereo should be silent. Awareness of the food itself should be paramount. When dining with the family or friends, do not discuss personal problems or bring up any heavy topic of conversation. Low voices and pleasant talk are the proper accompaniments to dining in the company of others. These are happy moments, a time when you are gathered in an atmosphere of warmth, nourishment, and love.

III

Once you have established a new nutrition and are eating less you should extend a lifetime diet to include regulation of everything that goes into your mouth. All your improvements could be ruined by ill-considered use of alcohol or tobacco. I shall return to these items in Chapter Five, where other types of consumption affecting consciousness are considered.

The stages of change that culminate in a lifetime diet may be seen as a gradual process of purifyng the body and mind. The process is not unlike a journey up a mountain. At the peak is a purity that releases new energy and helps rid your life of debility, disease, and premature aging. To control knowledgeably everything you put in your mouth lowers the risk of contaminating your body with chemicals, additives, and fraudulent foods. In the beginning, at the base of the mountain, you eat poorly. A step up you free yourself from devitalized and junk foods. Higher you are free of all commercially prepared food products. You have all but stopped drinking coffee and are developing the pleasant habit in herbal teas. You do not use tobacco and only occasionally a glass of wine or beer. When you rid your diet of red meat you are higher, and higher still when you rarely ever eat flesh. At the summit, you eat only natural foods and regularly fast. You have a communion with preparing what you eat. You have risen above the ordinary plagues.

For myself, as I have indicated, scaling the mountain was a project of many years that called forth and simultaneously replenished discipline and determination. As I slowly and haltingly shed the habits of white flour, sugar, red meat, coffee, tobacco, and hard liquor, I began to enjoy more abundant energy. Cooking for myself, I got free of other tyrannies. I required less sleep and had more time to explore the inner self—the friend it took so long to find. As I opened this exploration my awareness increased still more. A new sense of my life that came from within needed direction, and I was ready for and capable of greater expectations.

CHAPTER FOUR

Relaxation and Meditation

Meditation has been misunderstood in this country, especially because of the simplified commercialized versions.... people have come to regard it as sort of 15 minutes of drugless bliss. ...[but] that's not really what meditation is about. Meditation is a way of reorganizing oneself internally, psychologically, emotionally, and even, perhaps, spiritually, if you can use that word without making it religious.*

Rudolph Ballentine, M.D.

I

A workable exercise program that is appealing and vitalizing combined with a lifetime plan of food consumption that furnishes a wholesome diet cannot help but produce a healthy, energized body and mind. One way or another many people accomplish this much. To go no farther would be regrettable, yet it seems that few people realize that the destination they seek lies beyond the accomplishments of exercise and diet.

Improving health and social functioning by instilling a regime of beneficial exercise and diet are necessary, but in and of themselves not sufficient to develop one's full potential for expanding consciousness. The next step in the journey back to the self, the ultimate migration, is to become mistress or master of one's own mind. The Indian yoga master Swami Rama says that all of the body is in the mind but not all of the mind is in the body. As you increase awareness and vitality of your psychosomatic self you are inevitably led to consideration of your psycho-spiritual self. This chapter deals with the difficult challenge of governing the mind and final problem of connecting daily life and living with the spirit. Meditation is the key.

I suggest that you begin the program of self-transformation by establishing disciplines of the body before taking up meditation, the mental discipline. I believe this is preferable for most people. Some choose to begin with meditation, perhaps because they feel no need to improve their physical condition. People who truly have no such need are quite rare, however, and the chances are great that were you to ignore exercise and consumption control and begin meditating regularly you would be led back to diet and exercise. The practice of learning to control your attention, for that is what meditation boils down to, is a very demanding one that calls for every advantage you can bring to it. Sooner or later you would come to appreciate the value of physical fitness on the one hand and, on the other, to see how much of a handicap numerous needless consumptions are.

We gather and focus the energy derived from exercise and consumption control in meditation and thereby achieve what seems impossible in our modern American lives. We meditate to center ourselves. We meditate to create distance from the chaotic psychological and environmental conditions in which we live. Although this is not its primary goal, meditation does help to develop awareness of what is required to better steer through times of confusion. Through this development we succeed in gaining control of our destinies. Meditation centers one on an inner essence whose genius is mastery of all that is petty and destructive in life so that one may go toward what is grand and constructive.

Meditation permits you to experience the truth that your body and mind are informed by and infused with the essence called spirit.

Meditation is the means that allows this truth to emerge into awareness, thereby enabling one to function as a whole person

---

whose body, mind and spirit abide in harmony and balance under all circumstances.

This in turn frees consciousness to enlarge even farther and opens you to new and greater realities.

There are brimming realms awaiting exploration.

There is a limitless potential to be uncovered and enjoyed.

By practicing meditation you learn to still the eternal (some say infernal) monologue inside your head. In the stillness you become aware of a certain presence. It is the self within whose existence had been buried under the noisy combustion that can ruinously hinder ordinary life. Your spiritual nature has always been there although it was denied recognition. Meditation enables you to heal this division of your totality.

Before saying more about this division, its origin and consequences, I need to point out the important, practical reason to meditate that cannot be overlooked by anyone, and that is the antidote it provides to the harmful effects of stress. Psycho-social stress is recognized as a major contributing factor in the development of high blood pressure and heart disease, cancer, arthritis, and many other so-called "afflictions of civilization," as noted by Kenneth Pelletier, author of *Mind as Healer, Mind as Slayer*. In the lives we lead stress cannot be avoided. To live the lives we choose stress need not be avoided, but it is of the utmost importance that stress be identified and controlled by *true* relaxation. Meditation is a superlative way to "unstress," to calm and restore to normal functioning those vital systems of your body that automatically raise alarms when presented with psycho-social stresses.

The illusory securities at risk during the daily pursuits of love and money, sex and politics, and threatened by the demands of materialism and professionalism can be seen for what they are through meditation. Too much of daily life today produces conflict, ambiguity, frustration, and discontent. Soothing flayed nerves with alcohol, Valium, or some other drug produces a deadly backlash. Escape into the mindless entertainments of television or movies offers no solution at all. Recreational activities such as bowling or backgammon, for example, and social activities such as dancing may provide some degree of stress relief but can never supply what is needed. Deeply restorative relaxation is essential to one's well-being and meditation is the best way to accomplish this vital task. Dr. Pelletier reviewed the scientific evidence on the subject and concluded as follows:

The preliminary research . . . indicates that the conscientious practice of meditation increases autonomic stability, aids in the habituation to repeated stresses, and produces a state of relaxation deeper in some respects than that induced during sleep. In addition, the characteristic physiological pattern of a person during meditation is virtually opposite to that of a neurophysiological stress pattern. These effects of the meditation can carry over and extend into the post-meditation stage of daily activity. These studies imply that regular meditation can be an effective means of stress alleviation.

Yet this, no more than insight into the conditions that harry us, is not the goal of meditation either. What the legions of modern medical science have recently begun to glimpse the poet Thoreau fully grasped a hundred years ago when he wrote: "Health requires this relaxation, this aimless life. This life in the present."

I will say more about this later in this chapter.

I believe it is useful to discuss and try to understand how our spiritual nature came to be submerged, cut off and divided from awareness. To cope successfully with the demands of social living our minds have been trained to work within boundaries. This has been going on since earliest childhood with the result that we have become exclusively committed to a linear, rational, and manipulative mode of thinking. This aspect of mind, the intellect, with its powers of reasoning and ability to deal with objects and relationships in space and time, enables us to get on in the world. It is geared to the conditions of social and material necessity and is essential to survival, but it is, nevertheless, only one aspect of mind. Other aspects— namely intuitive and spiritual modes of apprehending reality—are not essential to social functioning. Consequently, for the most part they are left undeveloped and they remain unopened, asleep. It is as if we have never explored the mansion of the mind, as if we lived in only one room, unconscious of the possibilities of other rooms, other worlds, oblivious to the magnificence of the whole. Our conditioned minds, the one room we know so well, reveal only very limited areas of reality. To remain asleep, unconscious to the whole, is to remain unfulfilled, living a meager, partial life such conditioning produces.

Many are quite unaware of this division. Others who do know of it know that it is as unnatural as it is unhealthy. There can be no true contentment or lasting satisfaction — only lethargy, frustration, and despair coupled with a constant yearning within ourselves — so long as a division between our mundane and spiritual selves prevails.

We are only half-alive, only partially grown, and we know it.

The objective conditioning of the rational mind is necessary for survival in the material world, but merely to survive is not to live a fully human life! *There is no mystery to materialism, but there is to human existence.* Meditation illuminates the enigma. It is free. It can be accomplished by anyone practicing alone. It is the most excellent approach to fulfilling that deep desire for something more. No deprogramming is necessary. The tools are relaxation and personal discipline. No matter who you are or where you are you can learn and use meditation to abolish division, to enter into and enjoy your full estate of living consciousness.

In the rush to capture the market of would-be meditators, some organizations have spread distortions about meditation. The notion, for example, that only one kind of meditation can change one for the better, while others cannot, masks the basic sameness of all meditation techniques.

Daniel Goleman
The Varieties of the Meditative Experience

II

What is meditation? Often meditation is confused with prayer or contemplation. A simple way of differentiating is to see that prayer and contemplation are objective, whereas meditation is totally nonobjective. In prayer one is usually following a form, invoking some deity or power outside of oneself in order to ask help or to express gratitude. In contemplation attention dwells on an object, we contemplate a problem, or a lover, a financial situation, perhaps the countryside, a mountain, or flowers. Prayer and contemplation can be rich and helpful in focusing thoughts or conditions, but they are not meditation.

Meditation is nonobjective. Your attention has no focus; one abides in a "choiceless awareness," to use Krishnamurti's words. The need to retrain attention to this end, according to Goleman, "is the single invariant ingredient in the recipe for altering consciousness of every meditation system." We need to transcend all thought and mental impression. We must withdraw attention from the chatter of mind so that all the worries and cares as well as the victories and glories of ego are cut off. It is rather like turning off the furnace, shutting down all the heat of human desire and involvement. By ceasing to pay attention to ego concerns you cause them to fade and extinguish. You have turned off one big switch of the world—all of Russia, Africa and Washington, D.C., your home, your job, all the inferiors and friends, lovers and creditors in your life. You forget those who pollute the world and those cleaning it up. As you switch off television and the picture sinks and the image is lost, so you may do the same with the self through meditation. For a time you are lost to the mundane world and enter a state of wondrous comfort and quiet. *This is the point where the continuum of stress effects is severed.*

Your mind may bathe in colors you have never envisioned, images never before seen may appear. You may experience sensations of floating or soaring. Conversely, you may feel physical discomfort. Your foot falls asleep and begins to prickle, your nose itches and wants scratching, your back aches or your stomach rumbles with hunger. All these experiences too, whether painful, irritating, delightful or scary, will pass away as you continue to withhold attention from them. Remember that, unlike contemplation or prayer, meditation has no object. Eventually, if you persist and if your zeal matches in intensity the purity of your endeavor, you become aware of a limitless, totally alive and dynamic void. There arises with clarity the wordless convicton that you are one with this infinitude. It is at this moment that meditation creates the spiritual connection. That which you become aware of as all encompassing is your spirit, an inner you, the you that links with and is not different from eternal spirit.

This knowledge confirms a center that is love and, if you are open to it, love will fill your being. Love is the highest state of being. Love is what is positive in life and no matter who we are, no matter what age, we hunger for it. It is a mystical need, the link with the spiritual. We connect body, mind and spirit and in this state of love are united to others who are so connected.

Access to that conviction concerning who you are does not belong to a chosen few or a particular sect. It is freely open to all who know how to seek it. Religion or organization are quite unnecessary. Meditation has no certified origin. The tradition reaches into the West as well as the East. It was ancient when history began. You do not have to join or believe in anything. It is a natural gift, an innate ability each individual has, an ability that will transport you toward the heights of expanded consciousness.

There is no one approved method of meditation. No single text could encompass the entire magnitude of meditation or, for that matter, consciousness. If you feel the need to receive instruction, to join a meditation class or attend a seminar or workshop, by all means do so. The best you can do with such instruction is to discern and assimilate the basic techniques as practiced by meditation masters. But any individual should be wary of both shortcuts and dogmatic systems. Meditation practiced in a religious context or embedded within a quasi-scientific system usually requires an emotional allegiance that is unnecessary.

It is regrettable that awareness and consciousness are merchandised these days, for they are free and as much a birthright as breathing. However, this should not dissuade you from investigating means and methods because, as with breathing, you can learn from those who have devoted many years of study to the subject. But whoever your teachers are and whatever method you begin with, you will eventually discover you have a spiritual teacher inside yourself who will lovingly guide you if you will listen and trust. For many the notion of an external guru is a seductive myth, yet a true master is one who puts you in touch with yourself, opens you to yourself and to the teacher within you. Beyond that, with rare exception, the role of pupil to master, of servant to saint, can be dangerous. It can be a cruel game that ensnares you in a powerful ego that preys on innocence and ignorance and a troubled self.

Trust in yourself.

Learn and discover a method best suited to your personality and environment and your aims in life. A sincere desire to meditate and to understand the value of centering will produce this method.

How can you go talking so
quietly, head downwards?. . .
"What does it matter where my body happens to be?"
He said, "My mind goes on working all the same."

Through the Looking Glass

The basic requirements for meditation concern your body and the environment. In seated meditation the upper body needs to be relaxed but not saggingly so, the back erect but not rigid, while the lower body provides a solid, stable base. Strength and awareness are required to hold the torso and head upright. Never strain. Do not suck in your belly military-style. The natural curve of your lower spine must be respected. Keep your chin tucked in and your ears in the same line as shoulders and hips. This positioning aligns and keeps open the thorax and chest for maximum ease of breathing. Focus on keeping your shoulders in the same plane as your hips and the whole weight of your head centered over and balanced on the top of the spine. You may sit comfortably on an armless chair having a firmly cushioned seat, using the forward third or so to support your buttocks and placing your feet flat on the floor. Or sit on the floor, using the forward third of a fairly firm cushion to support your buttocks. In either position relax your shoulders and place your hands comfortably on your lap. Always remember to keep the back and head erect. Whichever position you choose, whether on a chair or on the floor, take a few moments to seat yourself so that you are perfectly stable and at ease and not inclined to move, for the prime requisite of meditation is to remain dynamically still.

You may wish to vary seated meditation postures with the "corpse" pose, described in the exercise chapter on page 80, in which you lie flat on the floor. It should be noted that the problem of falling asleep arises when using this pose for meditation. Nevertheless, many claim that this position has an advantage in that the body enjoys the greatest level of tension reduction.

With reference to sitting on the floor, the question arises: what to do with the legs? The classic solution is called the lotus pose with right foot atop left thigh, heel against groin and left foot atop right thigh, heel against groin and knees on the floor. Here the hands are composed in the classic Zen manner. The half-lotus pose should not be forced. Unless one has been sitting this way from adolescence, say, when physical growth is virtually complete yet the bones, muscles and tendons are still supple and highly educable, very few people, whether Asian or Westerner, can even get into this position much less be comfortable in it for any length of time. It is considered the ultimate posture for meditation because it provides the most stable base. If you experiment with the lotus or half-lotus pose, move gently! If they prove too difficult, abandon them.

One alternative is the so-called Burmese positioning in which legs are folded parallel to one another, knees resting on the floor.

If any of these positions work for you, fine, but most people, especially in the beginning, should simply sit in whatever folded-legs manner is natural and comfortable for them. Here are a few exercises that will help you stretch and strengthen the leg muscles used in sitting on the floor.

Sit on the floor. Bring the soles of your feet together. Take hold of your toes with your hands and gently pull your feet toward you, using your elbows to work your knees down toward the ground—pull-push, pull-push—for a minute or more.

Sit on the floor and put your legs out straight in front of you. Place your right foot on the thigh above your left knee. Use your right hand to work your knee up and down. After a minute or so, reverse your position and do the same with the other knee.

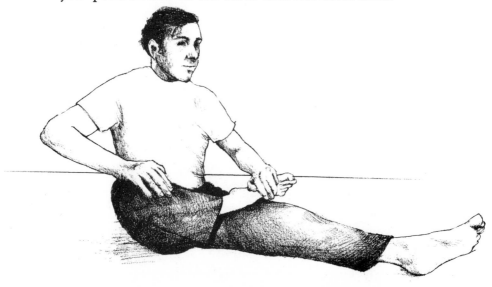

Sit on the floor. Alternately, with legs out straight in front of you, place the sole of your right foot against the thigh above your left knee. Use your right hand to work your knee up and down; after a minute or so, reverse your position and do the same with the other knee.

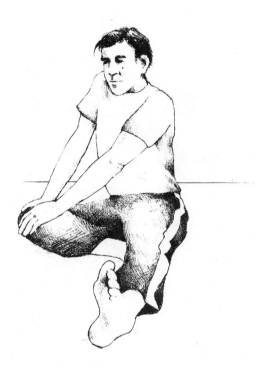

The meditation posture I prefer is to sit on the floor with a cushion tucked comfortably underneath me. My legs are bent toward the crotch, the soles of my feet turned upward and one heel resting on top of the other. The cushion is adjusted so that my knees rest on the floor with ease and my back is straight.

Each person will want to experiment with the various possibilities to find the best one according to her or his height and physical proportions. Be tolerant, gentle, and patient with yourself. Above all, do not get caught up in any ideas about the "right" way to sit. Many attach a certain hauteur to sitting in the classic manner but this has nothing to do with meditation, per se. The aim is to position the upper body and head so that they are erect, to find a stable base, then to forget the body. This is why you never meditate until two or three hours after eating. This is why you wear light, loose clothing or, if the room is warm enough, no clothing at all. I recommend beginning with a basic honesty by baring the body. We spend most of our lives covered and armed by garments and tend to forget that within these layers of fabric and fashion there is a warm and pulsating body. Meditating in the nude can make you that much more aware of your whole physical reality.

It is believed that the ideal time to meditate is in the early hours of the morning. On arising, if possible, go for a short, brisk walk or a jog. Bathe or shower to refresh yourself, then, in those hours before the electricity of the workaday world begins, meditate. This means getting up earlier, but a program of exercises should help. One of the changes brought by developing awareness is that you begin to end each day before midnight. Occasionally this is not possible, but you should try to do so whenever you can in order to take advantage of the early morning. Not enough can be said for the quiet hours between four and seven AM. From a practical standpoint they offer more privacy than any other time of the day, but they also have qualities which are not apparent until experienced. Less traffic is running, less electricity is being used. Phones are silent, few people are about, above all, the sky and the air are different, as sweet and clean as may be. Sometimes these are the only hours when it is possible to hear birds sing.

At first it may be difficult to establish this routine, but once you have you will not want to change. Conversely, some may get into it easily and enthusiastically but find their resolve to carry on begin to wane. A moderate degree of enthusiasm is certainly desirable, but it is unwise to get excited about beginning a meditation habit. Remember, it is a *habit* you wish to establish. Slow but sure is the course; steadiness and resolution are the most helpful attitudes. Before long—probably within the first few weeks—the rewards will amply repay your effort. One of the first things you notice is that since meditating is rejuvenating, you will require less sleep. Also, it becomes easier to master the day before it begins.

If you are unable to meditate in the morning, find another time of the day. Doing so just before bedtime is fine providing you are not too tired or sleepy and have not eaten for two to three hours. Many choose to meditate after work and before dinner. Again, refresh yourself by bathing or showering beforehand and do a few minutes of gentle exercise to release the tensions of the day. Then, meditate. How much better to meditate and renew the energies of your being than to stupefy the stressed self with alcohol! Whatever hour of the day works best for you keep to that time, for this will help establish the habit. Meditate every day, even if only for fifteen or twenty minutes. Have a clock or watch placed where you can see it without having to move. One-half to three-quarters of an hour would be best. If a daily routine seems too much in the beginning, meditate three days of the week, always keeping to the same days.

Meditate alone in a quiet room that is neither too dimly lit, which might foster dozing off, nor too bright, neither too warm or too cool. Master meditators do not need such arrangements. In India yogis can sit in the middle of Calcutta traffic and meditate, but you are not in India, nor are you a yogi. You live in the Western world and should eliminate or minimize distractions. You will have enough problems to contend with.

Silence the telephone.

Lock the door.

Many can establish a place in the office for meditation. Years ago I knew the calm, kind director of an import and export firm. Every day, a half-hour before his luncheon, he hung a Do Not Disturb sign on his door and instructed that no calls be put through to him. Knowing only this much I kidded him about his afternoon naps. He looked at me and smilingly shook his head.

"I'm doing something far better," he said. "I'm meditating."

The reply made little impression. I had often envied his unfailingly kind manner and wondered how a man with his responsibility managed to remain so relaxed and in such good spirits, but I went on for years without connecting his personality with his meditating.

Getting together with other people who meditate can be very supportive, especially in the beginning. Group meditation itself can be very powerful. It puzzles me why no one has begun to franchise meditation parlors: sensible, attractive, soundproof places arranged with a proper regard for privacy, ventilation, and lighting where anyone could go for any period of time and rent a space in which to meditate, or purchase basic, nonsectarian instruction on how to meditate. If this facility were equipped with a sauna, a masseuse, and areas in which one could exercise, so much the better.

Once you learn you can meditate anywhere—on a bus or an airplane, on a park bench or at a beach—but it is important to begin in a quiet, personal place that is reserved for work on yourself. It is helpful to create an environment for meditation that is inviting to you and enhances your practice. If you are lucky enough to have a spare room make this into a meditation and exercise center. Few furnishings are required: a thick rug, a fairly hard cushion or, if your prefer, an armless chair. If your floor covering is not thick enough, make a mat by folding a soft blanket or use a few large bath towels. Let this place be your retreat where, for an hour or two every day, you can shut the world off and attend to yourself. The room should be well-ventilated and the lighting soft. If possible, the room should be home to green plants and favorite prints or a painting you especially like. If you do not have a spare room an area in another room can be adopted and reserved for the purpose. Make it a personally pleasing place. Burn incense or scented candles to change the air and qualify the atmosphere, for this is the place from which you will begin to journey toward the precious essence of your being.

I place emphasis on atmosphere because so many elements of our modern environment are antagonistic to the regular practice of meditation. Especially in the beginning, I believe it is important to set aside time and properly prepare one's place and oneself. No matter where my travelling job takes me I try to create an atmosphere conducive to meditation. I improve the atmosphere of a hotel room in whatever way I can. It is marvelous what incense can do after the room has been cleared of advertisements, telephone books, and those room-service order forms usually placed to catch the eye. I sweep these away in a drawer and get the telephone out of sight under a bed pillow. There is nothing to be done about the glassy eye of the television. Sometimes I drape a robe over it, otherwise I simply turn my back to it. I order flowers or pick some up from a nearby stand. I usually carry a small tape recorder and play a Steven Halpern or Paul Horn tape. A hot bath, music, and the incense prepare an environment. The lingering effects of the crowded, sometimes frantic, conditions of my job are dissipated. To complete my restoration and renewal, I meditate.

III

Breathing and Devices

Meditation has numerous ways of reproducing its effects. Once begun, it spreads and develops as a source of incredible relaxation and renewed confidence in your need to be nothing more than what you are. In order to take advantage of this it is best to learn how to facilitate the habit.

After you have established the appropriate atmosphere, begin to incorporate the basic fundamentals of breathing and exercise. Alternate nostril breathing described on p. 75 will relax and calm you. The neck rolls on p. 78 and the eye exercises on p. 77 will release tension. Now close your eyes and breathe deeply. Slowly fill the diaphragm and chest, slowly breathe out, allowing the chest and diaphragm to contract.

Always, always breathe through your nose.

Feel as if you are breathing from the pit of your belly. Do not squeeze the nostrils when inhaling. Breathe naturally. Focus your effort for a few moments time on your breath so that you breathe in a certain rhythm, breathing in to the count of eight, breathing out to the count of eight. In breathing in and out do not hunch your shoulders. Keep your back and head comfortably erect.

Nothing about meditation should be forced.

Keep your eyelids lowered, allowing your gaze to rest on the floor a foot or so in front of you. Give your attention solely to the breath.

There are two distinct tones as you breathe in and out. The yogis say the incoming breath sounds like *sa* and the outgoing like *hum.* In Sanskrit these sounds means "Thou art That," but do not dwell on meaning. Simply breathe and give this breath undivided attention.

Breath is the present moment flowing through you. The practice of meditation has no past or future. Its goal, if one may call it a goal, is to escort awareness into the timelessness of here-and-now.

Focusing your sole attention on the breath is far from easy. Lawrence Le Shan, in his helpful book *How to Meditate,* said it well: "The first shock of surprise comes when we realize how undisciplined our mind really is: how it refuses to do the bidding of our will. After 15 minutes of attempting only to count our breaths and not be thinking of anything else, we realize that if our bodies were half as responsive to our will as our minds are, we would never get across the street alive."

The act of breathing is unique among physiological functions in that it may transpire without awareness yet it may also, with the merest effort of will directing attention, be brought to consciousness. Sustaining that effort without pause, however, is the rub. Attention keeps slipping away. Now you have it; now you don't. Keeping the focus requires infinite, second-by-second care. You will be amazed and perhaps disheartened to discover how little control you have over your attention. Persist. As Le Shan rightly pointed out, "The important thing about meditation is how hard and consistently you work on it, not how 'well' you do it." He tells a story about one Saint Bernard of Clairvaux who, when asked about the successfulness of his lifetime meditation practices, replied: "Oh how rare the hour and how brief its duration!"

I repeat, it is hard to withdraw and keep withdrawn, all attention from the monologuing mind. This is what you seek, but interruptions will occur over and over again. Over and over again you will have to reestablish attention on the two tones of breathing. Another difficulty arises. Bringing your breathing into consciousness is not the same as consciously breathing. The latter means that you are controlling your breath and, except when you wish to practice certain techniques of special breathing, the aim is simply to witness the natural ebb and flow of breath, to let it be. Similarly, make no effort to suppress thoughts, for that would be self-defeating. Tibetan Buddhist meditation master Chogyam Trungpa, in an excellent collection of his lectures to beginning students entitled *Meditation in Action,* advised about the thoughts that inevitably arise that "one should just try to see the transitory nature, the translucent nature of thoughts. One should not become involved in them, nor reject them, but simply observe them and then come back to the awareness of breathing. The whole point is to cultivate the acceptance of everything, so one should not discriminate or become involved in any kind of struggle."

Accepting everything, anticipating nothing, letting all be as it will, you follow the instant-by-instant flow of your breath. Beneath the waves on the surface of the sea the water remains massively calm. Be like that calm.

Uncle, how can words that *have no meaning even for the person who utters them be of any use at all, let alone assist his spiritual progress?. . ."*
Groping for a way of expressing his thought in English, he replied earnestly: "Words with meanings just good for ordinary use—not much power and get in your way like

rocks upsetting a boat. Words with much power not show out real meaning—best forget meaning and keep mind free."

John Blofeld
Mantras, Sacred Words of Power

Although attention to breathing has for centuries been the favorite device for focusing attention during meditation practice, the use of mantras also has a long history and has recently gained popularity here in America thanks to the spread of Transcendental Meditation, which employs this device as the centerpiece of its method. The word mantra is Sanskrit and means, approximately, prayer or hymn. A mantra is a short formula of sacred words. By continuous silent repetition of a mantra one excludes all other thoughts from the mind. The initiates of Transcendental Meditation receive in secret a mantra of Sanskrit syllables that have no literal meaning. The meaninglessness of the mantra is in keeping with ancient tradition. Some say that the power of a Sanskrit formula resides within the sounds themselves and the physical vibrations they set off in the body of the practitioner. Whether or not there is any truth in this mystical view, I have found that the mental repetition of any short phrase is an effective device for focusing attention.

The phrase need not be bestowed on one, nor be meaningless or foreign. A good mantra-like device could be the words, "I am one with all," for example. John Blofeld, a respected Chinese scholar, who has made a study of mantras, thinks that the Jesus Prayer qualifies as a mantra. Its meaning, like the meaning of the phrase I suggest above, blurs and fades with constant repetition so that one's attention is not nagged by the verbal concept it signifies. It runs, "Lord Jesus Christ, Son of God, have mercy on us." If you find yourself particularly disturbed about one thing or another, so riled emotionally that you cannot calm yourself by attention to breath, try using a mantra in your meditation practice. I cannot recommend that you use the mantra exclusively, however, for the problem with the mantra is that it is difficult to get rid of once a meditative habit is secured.

Another device for achieving an inward focus, and one that I personally find helpful, is visualization. Simple or elaborate, the possiblities are numerous. They should be investigated, I think, only after one has firmly established a meditation habit. In the beginning or in consolidating a meditation habit it is best to use only three symbols: the circle, the square, or the triangle. Using one of the three, close your eyes and let your mind see only the symbol. Do not study it. Do not expand or detail it. Use it to pass through.

Colors are excellent visualizations. Close your eyes and visualize a soft and benevolent blue mist. Breathe in the mist. Let its purity soothe and calm you. Or you may visualize yourself in a faraway golden green meadow. In the visualization seat yourself comfortably for meditation. In this peaceful place nothing can disturb you. Allow its dynamic stillness to flow through you.

Elaborate forms of creative meditation should only be considered after you have become established in the habits of exercise, diet, and basic meditation. Creative meditations are a development that, I believe, should only be entered into after one has had considerable practice in centering within. I use the following method, which might be tried when you feel your meditative habit established in this way.

Sit relaxed.

Spine erect.

Breathe slowly and deeply.

Repeat "I am completely relaxed, I completely let go."

Visualize a tiny dot of light in the middle of your forehead between your eyes.

Focus all your attention on that dot, that point between the eyes. Concentrate. At first it becomes a tiny spot of light that is hardly visible. Keep concentrating on it and breathe deeply as you do so. When your attention is completely focused on that spot of light you will no longer be aware of your breathing. Let the spot grow larger and shine brilliantly.

Just be a witness. Do not try to control it, do not try to make it grow. Soon it will fill your forehead. Lose yourself.

Let the light grow and grow.

The light is you. It is the presence of the spirit in you. Open yourself and let it shine in every cell of your body. Glow with it.

You will feel marvelously energized after this meditation. Seeing the light, bathing in the light, connects you with your inner energies, the energies empowering your total being. You can use this meditation to open channels blocked by stress or anxiety, the true causes behind every illness. Visualize these white-light energies flowing smoothly throughout your body, infusing every cell, harmoniously unifying your whole being. In this respect, meditation is a tool for healing ourselves. Not only in body and mind but in spirit as well, for it brings to enlivening awareness the essence that pervades each of us.

IV

The initial contact with one's spiritual self is one of complete elation. It is unutterably wonderful to rediscover your full dimensional self. Your newly expanded consciousness now includes a part of you that had been unknown for so long. A door has been opened and you have experienced the wonder beyond. Now you know other realities and patterns.

You become available to energy which allows you to live a more meaningful life than you have ever known. The life you have been living, the dreary cycles of fear and loneliness, evaporate like bad dreams in the brilliant light of expanding consciousness. The bondage you had become accustomed to has ended.

This elation, this intoxication, will gradually subside to be replaced by an ongoing sense of profound fulfillment. The problems and challenges of daily life still confront you but you are changed now and you meet them differently. You have slain the dragons of pettiness, pointlessness, and despair. Win, lose, or draw in the arena of daily affairs, your center is solid and immovable. *You know who you are.* As the sages say, you are in the world but not entirely of it. You are of a piece with the cosmos.

Meditation makes us aware of how the life we have been living limits, indeed, separates us from the very concept of consciousness. We have strayed too far from love and loving. Like ignorant children we have indulged in inane pursuits that have kept us plying the circular route of pleasure and pain. We have gone out instead of going in and by doing so have drifted from our centers and denied the existence of the wondrous living presence within.

Meditation shows that all this might have been necessary. As you must travel away from home to discover how precious home is, so it seems somehow to have been necessary for you to live a conditioned experience in order to yearn for the unconditioned and limitless estate to which you were born. That is why you must be *ready* for meditation. Not until you feel the need to know yourself, to center, to gather in your energies, will meditation be undertaken with resolve and determination. Once resolved, however, nothing can stop you. Be who you are wherever you are. There is no need for a sect, an ashram, or a cave on a mountain. Your ground is the ordinary, everyday world of the twentieth century, glutted with materialism and riddled with stress. But you have a refuge. Your own body, mind, spirit is the vehicle of transcendence.

Do not be misled into believing there is something very solemn and special about this practice of meditation. Nothing could be more natural to who you really are, where you truly live.

Meditation is nothing but coming back home, just to have a little rest inside. It is not the chanting of a mantra, it is not even a prayer; it is just coming back home and having a little rest. Not going anywhere is meditation, just being where you are; there is no other 'where'—just being there where you are, just occupying only that space where you are.

Bhagwan Shree Rajneesh
Only One Sky

The journey is not easy. Meditation, the key tool, is difficult and its practice requires great patience and perseverance. It requires discipline, learning and certain changes in your life before it will bring changes that you could not have planned for, could not even have imagined. Remember that the disciplines you practice through exercise and diet begin the changes. As they conserve your body, meditation restores your spirit. The choice is yours. You can stay unconscious, asleep, and unaware or you can seize the means of change. The rendezvous with inner connections is up to you.

CHAPTER FIVE

Lifestyle

If it strikes the reader as presumptuous to equate his personal center with the center of the cosmos, he must be reminded that physics requires him to do just that; because space is relative and curved, the center of the physical universe is for each observer the point from which his observations proceed.

Huston Smith
Forgotten·Truth

I

"Lifestyles" refers to the tangible and intangible modes which encompass your whole life. Included are the attitudes, values, and priorities you hold as well as the environment you live in and its material and psychological features. Your lifestyle both expresses and determines your individuality. Much of it is fixed and not subject to alteration but certain crucial elements can be changed to agree with your desire to expand awareness and participate more in living consciousness.

A lifestyle reflects a person's family background, the ethnic and regional inputs made during the formative years of childhood, and the religious, educational, and socio-economic conditions that shaped her or him. Later determinants include the geographical area and particular community in which the person resides, the profession, occupation, the apartment or house inhabited. Further elaborations are created by choices of home furnishings, clothes, transportation, the uses of leisure time as well as the particular people and social activities she or he prefers. It is these latter categories and elaborations that may be altered, provided the person is willing to examine the attitudes and values that sustain them. As always, the changes that matter proceed from the center within. "Give me a place to stand on," said an ancient Greek thinker, "and I will move the earth."

It is possible to follow a certain lifestyle and yet be alienated from all that it represents. Playing themselves false, such people have come to identify with the various personas their lifestyle automatically provides. They become so attached to family, career, possessions, and ambitions that they utterly forget their true identity, the mind-body-spirit self that alone imparts meaning to their relationships and activities. To cling to the trappings of life and ignore its essence induces frustration and dissatisfaction. The multitudinous involvements in careers, families, friends, communities, entertainments, politics and the dunning of religion confer a mad, repetitious cycle of distractions that conflicts with true awareness and, indeed, leads far away from inner peace and harmony. Such people whirl in endless rounds of activity, afraid to miss out, to be left out or rejected, to be alone. Involvement becomes a stupefying alternative to awareness.

Even those of us who have begun to develop awareness often find it difficult to recognize activities and involvements that have become habitual. The questions of what and how to do what you need to do can be endless and are best taken up one by one as they arise. I do not believe there can be any master plan but my own experience is that a systematic approach is very helpful. My approach is to examine and critically evaluate in turn the person, the home, and society. Bear in mind that by developing awareness and moving to alter your lifestyle you will drop many traditional attachments. By creating disciplines for exercise, diet, and meditation you have already begun to explore the value of nonattachment, to be more self-contained, and to see the virtue in dropping certain relationships and discarding certain possessions. As you disengage and simplify your life, you gain the confidence of knowing that you can live without the hindering habits and fixed ideas to which you were once attached and by which, often, you were ensnared. Once this process of change has begun it will affect you and everyone and everything around you. Recognizing this and preparing for what is bound to happen is of paramount importance! You must be alert and responsible at all times and strictly avoid confusing or disorienting your loved ones and close associates. Awareness must be unified in such a way that the ensuing changes in your lifestyle are a victory and a blessing for the whole network of your relationships.

On the whole, any notion of exploring or taking a chance in relating with one's ego and projections is regarded as inspired by the enlightened mind. That is because you are not trying to hold on, to continue something, to prove something, but you are looking at other possibilities. That in itself is a very brave attitude and a very spacious one, because your mind is completely charged with curiosity and interest and space and questions. It is a sort of wandering process and is very hopeful and very positive in this particular connection.

Chogyam Trungpa
Glimpses of Abhidharma

We begin with the person. Begin by keeping a journal, which will greatly increase self-awareness of your activities and motives. Lengthy self-examination is not necessary, in fact, undesirable. Just make brief notes at the end of each day about what you did and why. Try to account for every waking hour, not in detail but in general. Every so often, read back over the past week or two and make a critical appraisal of how you are using your time and energy.

In my own case, I was shocked at the hours I wasted shopping: precious time spent seeking things I did not need. I was more shocked to admit that my shopping was a result of exposing myself to the infectious barrage of advertising. Not until I came to regard advertising as audio-visual pollution could I escape its effects, for I was often ensnared by the glitter of its cartoonish qualities, by the colorized electricity of its distortion. Eventually, painfully, I learned to cut out this pollution, moving from not being bothered by it to feeling extremely insulted that it was forced upon my attention with such rude frequency and bad taste. While driving with the radio silenced I discovered I could notice more. At home my love of music was satisfied by greater investment in records and tapes, and I drastically reduced television to very select programming of noncommercial channels. By conducting ordered evaluations in print media of what was available to fill my needs as they arose, I solved most of my shopping problems. There was no question of deprivation or missing out as advertisers would have me believe but a simple matter of carefully defining needs and, above all, protecting my privacy.

A journal will help you learn to use your energy wisely and conserve your privacy, but you must be honest in confronting motives and questioning your use of time. How much of what you do is to escape loneliness? How often are you killing time? Although such self-examination may be painful the rewards for purging anti-life attitudes are considerable. Be fair with yourself, not harsh. Do not be judgmental or condemnatory but try to *notice* how you live each day. Then decide, in the light of your long-range goal to expand awareness, what must be changed.

Another example from my own personal experience — as I came to use my time more productively and to cherish my privacy — was that I saw less of those people in my life who did not seem to understand and who occasionally mocked my interest in health and awareness. Harmful gossip, jaded or fatalistic remarks about finances or politics, morbid comments about the state of friends, introduced bad opera I did not need. Talk about acquisitions, recent sexual detente and current vogue pushed me toward the arenas of snarling competition from which I was determined to escape. Withdrawal from such relationships produced no regrets on either side, yet for those who wondered or sincerely inquired, I was available and glad to share my interests within the bounds I was gradually establishing for myself.

Certain activities that you may still indulge in are not only habitual but physically detrimental. I refer to the use of alcohol, nicotine, and caffeine. Although legal and socially acceptable, these three substances are at the same time lethal in the danger they pose to well-being and the havoc they sow in exchange for dubious rewards—relief when you are depressed and relaxation when you are satisfied. But these habits extract an intolerably high toll, for *they ultimately cancer the human anatomy.* Alcohol destroys more lives, ruinously squanders human energy, and costs populations more in financial devastation than any other substance. A cigarette not only tastes and smells bad, the United States Surgeon General flatly asserts that it is dangerous to your health. As for caffeine, a recent study at Vanderbilt University showed that the caffeine in just two or three cups of coffee shoots up blood pressure, slows, then speeds up the heart, speeds up breathing and the output of hormones that force the nervous system to work harder—all potential harmful effects.

Everyone who uses these substances knows they are both expensive and completely nonessential to existence. Yet people persist. This is because the user has made a choice of the attachment to the habit and the mood-changing effects, the highs they produce. *The key is that a similar choice of nonattachment can be made.* The habit is a product of accepted activity. To counteract this acceptance an unbiased witness is needed to provide a fresh perspective and enable a new awareness to emerge. One stands aside like a witness and watches her own repetitive reach for the next cigarette, for the additional cup of coffee, the second or third Bloody Mary. The witness sees that boredom, loneliness, or social pressure promotes these actions. In every likelihood it can be seen that a subtle addiction has taken hold. This view, this awareness may shock you! Good. Let it galvanize you into eliminating these acts from your repertoire. Only through a new awareness of the activity can the negative effects be seen with broad enough detachment, and only then can appropriate change be initiated.

The same detachment is needed to appraise the material things in your life. As you acquire habits and styles more in tune with your determination to develop awareness and expand and utilize consciousness, you will become skilled at consulting the witness and directing attention to the accumulation of furnishings that occupy your spaces and decide what is truly useful to the new realities and actions you are cultivating. Get rid of what is not useful. Clutter of any kind hinders your progress. You can live a larger life by eliminating "things" you may once have considered to be necessary or even fine and nice to have—"things" that are the legacy of materialism that subverts how you live. Call on the witness often and heed the counsel of detachment. Making reassessment your guiding principle will allow you to create an increasingly open environment in which both deep meaning and light-filled enchantment enter into each day.

I *shall only look up and say, "who am I then?" Tell me that first, and then if I like being that person, I'll come up; if not, I'll stay down here till I'm somebody else.*

Alice in Wonderland

II

Expanded consciousness on any level, practical or otherwise, dissolves much of the familiar and leads beyond the known. Precisely because the newly emerging synthesis is full of promise, you are likely to experience some confusion and uncertainty in this process of transformation and transcendence. You may be dazzled by the fabulous potential of expanded consciousness—the alluring rainbow of possibility that includes the new paradigms found in physics, biofeedback, holistic healing, parapsychology, Eastern and Western religions, tarot, astrology, and the rich assortment of occult means and methods. At the same time, you feel ambivalent about the dissolution of external authority you have effected. How shall you decide which explorations, if any, to undertake?

There is no reason to feel threatened by any of the possibilities of consciousness, but there is every reason to be contained within yourself before exploring any of them. And there is every reason to remember that centering yourself must be based on a lifestyle of which you are the ultimate architect and judge. Uncertainty, doubt, or confusion can be resolved after consideration and meditation and through a balanced trust in how you feel about the question at hand, whether it be a matter of attending a seminar on reincarnation and past lives, participating in a Gestalt therapy workshop, or delving further into some event of religious significance. To establish and maintain your center is crucial. In particular, experimenting with drugs should not be attempted before this is accomplished. I am speaking of drugs used to alter consciousness, a category which begins with nicotine, caffeine and alcohol and climbs a scale past marijuana and hashish, up toward mescaline, peyote, and LSD.

I, personally, do not use drugs. I only meditate. However, I realize that for centuries people from many cultures and religions have used drugs as agents, devices or helpers in order to explore and go beyond their ordinary mind. Peyote and mescaline are part of the religious ceremonies of certain American Indian groups. In India ganja is used by some yogis and spiritual people. In *The Natural Mind,* Andrew Weil points out the fundamental fascination with altered states of consciousness, "We seem to be born with a drive to experience episodes of altered consciousness. This drive expresses itself at very early ages in all children in activities designed to cause loss or major disturbance of ordinary awareness." In the United States, the use of drugs (aside from alcohol) and the experience of altered states have been little understood and, for the most part, badly practiced. Also, of course, such usage is illegal although the prohibition has probably done as much to spur as to deter experimentation. The complete comprehension of altered states of consciousness is still well beyond us and has not been clarified by scientific or creative investigation. Knowing that many readers of this book will wish to use drugs or psychedelic agents, despite the illegality, I offer a few simple rules based on common sense.

1. In using any agent have respect for its properties. Do not allow it to overwhelm you. Keep dosage at a base minimum.

2. Alcohol should never be used with other agents. The moderate use of beer or wine in the evening with a meal should be the extent of alcohol use.

3. The most common agents, marijuana and hashish, are usually smoked. Be aware that smoking anything for any purpose is bad for the lungs and respiratory system. Marijuana and hashish are best prepared in tea or baked into cookies.

4. Mescaline and peyote should never be used without an experienced guide with whom good rapport has been established.

5. When seeking an altered state through an agent know what you are using and prepare for the experience through meditation and fasting.

6. Practical preparation—the when and where—should be considered along with deep respect for effects. "Tripping" for diversion or recreation is unnecessary for those truly concerned with the long-range problems of change.

Sound information on drugs and altered states is not readily available. It is inevitably lost in the confusion brought about by political and religious institutions that have tried to prejudice public opinion against altered states of consciousness. It is advisable that considerable time be spent reviewing books and articles and in asking respected opinions on the subject. The key is caution. No matter what your previous background or experience it is best to implement an exercise program, master a lifetime diet, develop your own habit of meditation, and be firmly centered in your chosen lifestyle before experimenting with altered states whether induced by drugs or religious experience.

Agents or devices may not be necessary. There is much evidence that highs induced by external means have little to do with raising consciousness and many authorities can be cited who say that no agent or device exceeds the power of meditation. Speaking on the use of drugs, the yogi Swami Muktananda has pointed out, "Meditation affects extremely refined sensory nerves for which drugs . . . are much too strong. Those nerves cannot even bear strong coffee. Furthermore, meditation is more intoxicating than drugs could ever be . . . far more potent than ganja." Any advantage agents might have would have to be measured against the potential effect that "tripping" might have on the routines of your normal existence. The seventh and final rule is as follows: *No experience should be sought which would disrupt the daily care of your body and mind or your relationships and livelihood.*

III

The foregoing has concerned inner aspects of the person as they relate to lifestyle, particularly the all-but-unconscious habits and long-held attachments that affect your beginning efforts and sensibilities. Again, the new awareness arising from your center is the basis of meaningful alterations of lifestyle. And these, in turn, will inform the changes deemed useful in the outer aspects of the person, some examples of which are considered below.

Make a survey of the surface of your body. Be aware of any irritated reactions of the skin or scalp that may be caused by allergies. These signals of discomfort should alarm you that what you are eating or using on your body may be wrong or harmful to your system. They can also be signs of stress. Integrating sound nutrition with daily exercise, an occasional fast, and meditation is the very best long-term way to take care of your skin and hair. I also recommend the use of natural products and hot baths for this purpose.

I believe women should stay away from most commercial cosmetics. It is far better to use skin cleansers, lotions, and deodorants that are not perfumed and are generally hypo-allergenic. From a book written by Kay Ludeman and Louise Henderson, *Resource Handbook on Allergies,* I learned of many natural items that are good for hair and skin. For example, aloe vera gel heals all kinds of irritations. It is the pure extract of the aloe vera plant, is quite inexpensive, and can be purchased in any well-stocked drugstore. The wholesome foods we eat not only provide nutrition but also can be used in skin and hair care. The authors offer many alternatives to commercial cosmetics.

---

1. Splash water on your face then lather on a handful of finely ground almonds or oats. Rinse with water and pat dry.

2. You can experiment with herbs, such as mint and parsley, as facial cleansers. Sage makes an excellent astringent wash. Herbs are also good for the hair as a natural rinse. Try rubbing a slice of raw potato or cucumber on your face before washing, or make a face mask out of mashed avocados, which are also good for the

---

hair as a conditioner. Mayonnaise massaged into the hair and left in place an hour before shampooing makes a great conditioner.

3. Pure almond or apricot oil is excellent as a skin emollient and can be used on both face and body.

These are but a few alternatives. Your local bookstore, library or health-food store will all offer marvelous material on the subject that you can consult for other suggestions.

Make-up is a glory as well as a social burden we women have had for centuries. Advertising has tried to condition us into believing that we cannot get along without it. Horror that you should ever find yourself without make-up! That attachment is formidable but not insurmountable. It is, after all, only one of many ways to enhance your appearance. Being aware of alternatives is another. It is easier to remember that true attraction, true beauty reflects from within. Your whole person can become enhanced by the changes you have brought on through the preparation of inner energy. Make-up becomes a superfluous luxury and its use should be modulated as your inner magnetism increases.

Baths should be a prime source of relaxation, especially after work. Men in particular rarely use the bath properly and seldom realize that the benefits of a bath are quite different from those of a shower. The running water of a shower is best for cleaning the body. Once cleaned, soaking in a hot bath is incomparably relaxing, particularly if ceremony is created through burning incense, dimming lights and using oils to melt tension and ego as well. Retreats to the sauna are even better. You might investigate the costs of installing a sauna at home; it can be a wise investment.

In the United States and Europe we are pressured by changing fashion to spend beyond our means for clothing. Not only are clothes expensive but they usually require special care, which can be a continual expense. Dress is central to one's expression of personality, yet we seldom think about why we dress as we do. Clothing both protects and adorns the body, but it should provide personal aesthetic pleasure that should come before any professional or social statement of who we are. In no case should it become a conduit into inescapable credit balances. Clothing should never be purchased on credit. One's wardrobe can be an attachment wherein there never seems to be enough of the right sort of shoes, suits, shirts, blouses, coats, hats, whatever—the desires are created by advertising that causes you literally to be wearing your debts.

Stop being victimized in this way. The more aware you become the more you see the value in shedding attachments to countless things that, year after year, do nothing but clutter you life.

Make a systematic evaluation of yourself, your wardrobe, and your home. Establish a plan in which you buy only what you need only when you need it. Do not fall into the traps of fashion. Choose apparel made of natural fibers, such as cotton and wool, when you can afford them. Although more costly than synthetic fabrics they tend to be more durable and more suitable for passing through the elusive internal changes we have discussed. Footwear is of the greatest importance. Buy for the health and comfort of your feet. Prepare to walk and wander more. All the elements of your dress should combine in a kind of neutral disguise in which you are perfectly at ease.

IV

The home is the second major area of lifestyle. There is always a need to reassess where you live, how you live there, and why. Are you satisfied where you are? Is it comfortable and pleasing to you or did you move into it for convenience or as an investment? The apartment or house you dwell in should be important as a *shelter*—not merely as an investment. It should be the refuge that provides you with privacy and atmosphere. With organized effort anyone can find another place in which she or he may create better shelter.

If you are married and/or live with children the problems of living awareness are increased. You will find a need for additional space in order to afford more privacy. You will want to plan for more room to accommodate children or a relative who lives with you. This may mean moving. In all likelihood it means moving into a less expensive neighborhood or away fron a city altogether, into the suburbs or countryside. In 1978 George Gallup reported that more than one third of America's city dwellers would like to move away from their cities, and one can assume that the desire for more space and privacy was an important reason. If you have such a wish, act on it. To give up a fashionable address for a larger, more practical dwelling in order to gain privacy and freedom from financial involvement can easily be misunderstood. However, spare yourself from long explanations or justifications to friends and associates. Make the decisions and follow those decisions with the appropriate moves. Just do it! In the long run, it will prove to be a sound and sensible step for those determined to escape the spiraling systems that engulf all of us.

Now and then I live on a houseboat in a quiet harbor tucked under two green foothills. I find solitude here and am able to get in tune with myself and nature. The ceaseless movement of the water and the calm circling of the gulls add to the inner silence I gather from my practice. This home provides a space of tranquility, a passageway to inner worlds. After fasting, after replenishing my energies, I am well-fortified to return to the world of travel and revolving traffic, the strain that goes with work and foreign cities. Although I am married and share another home with my husband, I find time to retreat to the houseboat and walk along an old railway track that overlooks San Francisco Bay. For hours I simply sit, gazing out across the water. The solitude puts me in touch with a natural order of earth, sky, and sea, and ultimately of my own being.

To make decisions opting for change seems simplistic and can be easily ridiculed. This seems to stem from a quality of fear that change creates. The varieties and circumstances are different for everyone and what needs to be done can range from complex questions of where to live to what to do with a pet that is unruly and difficult to have around. If you have such a pet, make a decision to find it another home or take it to an animal shelter. You may think this a tough suggestion, but it is better than continuing with the irritation of not being able to handle the animal. Ridding yourself of a bothersome pet does not mean you love animals less but that you have gained clear command of your inhabited spaces. Get another pet if you wish, one more suited to your task and environment. Birds can be loving companions who require a minimum of care and allow loving, positive vibrations. Fish can also bring calm to your living space. Cats are always allies of meditation.

Reevaluate all furnishings, the colors of your walls, your use of lighting and floor space, curtains and rugs. Furniture, an important aspect of your lifestyle, can always be rearranged, but do not hesitate getting rid of furniture that no longer serves a purpose. If you cannot sell it, call the Salvation Army to come and take it away. Think in terms of comfort and space rather than fashion or whatever material value a thing may posses. The colors in your home should soothe and aesthetically enhance your private environment. Repaint if necessary. It is relatively easy to do and can be an exercise in exerting control, not to mention the personal satisfaction of doing something to initiate change.

It is important to reconsider lighting. Install dimmers if you do not already have them. Unless you are reading or doing other close work, bright light is not needed. It is hard on the eyes, wastes electricity, and usually violates the atmosphere that you have tried to create. Dimmers allow you to control the level of light and adjust it to changing moods. Candles are excellent for softer lighting, and, if scented, can still the air as well. The use of stained glass adds delicate beauty to a window and wondrously changes the light in a room.

The most obvious addition to living space is plants. Not only do they add color and greenery, they help establish a rapport between you and nature and bring you back to balanced aspects of your life, because the right plants will thrive in any positive atmosphere of care. They, along with flowers, are delightful, silent companions that add oxygen to the air in your rooms. I treat them as special friends. I talk to them, play music for them, and let them know when I am leaving for a few days. They respond by producing their own magic.

When and wherever start a garden. Whether of flowers or vegetables or both, a garden takes you outdoors and adds to your rapport with nature, not to mention the exercise it affords. There is also a tremendous satisfaction in knowing that at least some of the food you eat is the product of your own effort and available right outside of your own door. It is surprising what a six-foot-square plot can produce. An interesting experiment to make is to compare a vegetable purchased at the store with the same kind grown in your own yard. Boil two pots of water. Place the store produce near one and go to your garden and pick its twin. Cook the two for equal amounts of time and serve separately. The difference is telling.

In earlier chapters I have spoken about two of the most important spaces in the home, the kitchen and the area used for meditating. I pointed out that the meditation area should be reserved exclusively for this activity. It is also advisable to restrict other areas of your home to specific activities: the dining room for meals; the living room for social gathering, conversation, and listening to music; a study or library for reading, journal-writing, keeping household accounts. A separate room for television viewing is a good idea, particularly if there are children or others in your household who watch regularly.

The omnipresent problem of attachment to objects and habits constantly needs to be reviewed and refined. It is one thing to become involved in discourse and contemplation about attachment—and quite another to reduce the lofty ideas and ideals down to a level where they make a difference in your life. Attachments can be elusive and painful as well as comic. Not only are we attached to objects or habits, but we can be attached by them.

Telephones are perhaps the best example. They have attached themselves to our lives as *the* means of communication. Yet they are not essential, merely convenient, and they are not always the best means of communication. A letter or postcard can replace the phone call and, for the most part, a good deal of business can be conducted more sensibly through the mails. Even as these alternatives are used, however, the telephone is connected in too many parts of most households. I found that when I began to practice meditation or wished to withdraw for a day of solitude, I could easily refrain from using the phone but could do little to escape its ringing. Smothering the phone under pillows helped muffle the noise so that I could ignore it and hold myself still until the ringing ceased, but my privacy or my meditative state had been ruptured by the intrusion. When I first thought about having the telephone put on a plug, I dismissed the idea as silly and extreme. Nevertheless, I overcame the hesitation and ordered a plug to be installed. The first time I unplugged the instrument to spend a day alone I could sense the difference of insured silence. It was a long weekend I had set aside for relaxation and meditation and it proved unforgettable. I felt released and used the time so profitably that I kept the telephone unplugged the whole weekend long. It was an emotional vacation. I recovered my old journal and brought it up-to-date. When I went to the grocery I decided to leave my car at the curb and walk. After shopping I rode a bus back home. I had not used a bus in years. It took me back to my girlhood when, as a teenager, the bus was my only means of transportation.

Now the freedom from the hassle of driving and parking felt luxurious! It brought me to my senses, literally.

The pleasures of walking in quiet districts, like the serenity of a day of undisturbed silence, have been all but forgotten by many people. Unless we take direct action to avoid it, we will be continuously bombarded by the clangor of machinery and by systems that electronically suck at the vulnerable surface of our attention. After having the disconnecting plug installed in the phone I experimented further by disconnecting the radio and television for a three-week period and reducing my newspaper subscription to the Sunday edition. These moves were great fodder for the jokes of cynical friends, but to me they proved telling. I had somehow permitted myself to become enslaved by the technologies of the day. Worse, I was paying them to do it to me. These changes, small though they may seem, released me from enthrallment. The quality of my privacy deepened and the territory of my home widened in a way I had not thought possible. I urge you to try these things for yourself. You may find as I did that, after all, there is nothing to lose but your chains.

V

The key to having the lifestyle you want is to recapture control of what you do and where you do it. It is the formation of a process through which a person begins to live those actions usually relegated to the edges of wishful thinking. In this section we will look at some of the major contact points between an individual lifestyle and the surrounding society and examine practical ways to transform wishes into reality.

The best place to begin is to train yourself out of credit. Credit is never advantagous to the user! Buy-now-pay-later is the sly trap of your tomorrows. Next week, next month, next year — how smoothly the system operates to get you to surrender your options for the future. It may take one or two years or even more to turn your life around in this respect, but it can and must be done. As you have developed discipline in performing exercises, in changing your diet, in learning to meditate, so you must develop discipline in handling money. Money is green energy and unless you establish control over it, it will consume you. Make a determined effort by destroying your credit cards. If you must have credit standing, limit the number of cards to one or two. Keep a gasoline card, say, and a travel card such as American Express. Get rid of those all-purpose bank cards. Pay with cash or use traveler's checks. All it requires is that you spend more time with your personal budget. For the average person this should provide a welcome review of expenditure, which, in turn, will disclose patterns of spending. These patterns can be analogous to those of time and energy. As the lifelong consumption of white sugar poisons the body, the use of credit paralyzes the occupational freedom of the individual. With the same slow, insidious infection the use of credit builds a never-ending network of compromise that subverts the possiblity of change. Like the national debt, personal credit has become a plague from which only the aware individual can escape.

Living within one's income is an old-fashioned social value that is also an important principle for those striving to gain and remain in control of their lives. Another social value I subscribe to is captured in the slogan, "A day's work for a day's pay." Your means of livelihood consumes a large portion of every day. Whatever your job is, do it conscientiously, the best way that you know how. The corporation, profession, craft or service field within which you carry out your work may not deserve your best, but your self-respect does. At the same time, however, your livelihood should be kept separate from your private life. Maintain both in such a way that you enjoy a diversity of contacts, people from all walks of life, including people who are not working on the development of awareness. Some assessment of how much a job takes from the private life should be made. Dedication to a job to the degree that it increases stress is the tragic basis of the materialistic trap. Recent research has shown that job promotion can induce stress, which may, in turn, increase the possiblity of heart attack or cancer. There is a need to devote attention to preserving the meaning of your life. You are not living *for* a profession, a product, or corporation, or even *for* your family or community. You are living *with* these aspects. It is not difficult to separate what you do from who you are or what you want to do. Balancing the demands of job involvement against time needed for inner development is a necessary practice. Some withdrawal may be advisable to establish the balance wherein you are always in command of your activities.

The person who sets out to live consciously begins in a world she or he really cannot do anything about. Science promised us the earth, but its technologies are dooming us with pesticides and pollutants, and political and business leaders employ these technologies on a trial-and-error basis. In spite of the grave mistakes of the past many of them want to go ahead with nuclear power. In these massive controversies where error can lead to wholesale catastrophe, individual awareness can be whirled away: it cannot be forgotten. As with the pollution of air and water and the cutting down of forests, there seems to be nothing you can really do about righting the wrongs, but this does not mean you can cease to care and hope to create change. The environment of your home and neighborhood is immediate and, in these times, that of your country and the world is only slightly less so. Only as you discover meaning within yourself can you find it in your world. Jung wrote:

> . . . war has thrown out the unanswerable accusation to civilized man that he is still a barbarian, and at the same time it has shown what inflexible retribution lies in store for him whenever he is tempted to make his neighbor responsible for his own bad qualities. Yet the psychology of the individual corresponds to the psychology of the nations. What the nations do each individual does, and as is the individual, so is the nation. Only in the change of attitude of the individual can begin the change in the psychology of the nation.

The discovery of personal purpose renews the faith that we can effect the needed reforms and uphold the ethics of humanism in our world.

The rise of consciousness is viewed with alarm by some social critics. It has been argued that the interest in consciousness has "serious social consequences." Here is Christopher Lasch, writing in *The New York Review of Books:*

> The retreat to purely personal satisfactions—such as they are—is one of the main themes of the seventies. A growing despair of changing society—even of understanding it—has generated . . . a cult of expanded consciousness, health and personal growth. . . . Having no hope of improving their lives in the ways that matter, people have convinced themselves that what matters is psychic self-improvement: getting in touch with their feelings, eating health foods . . . jogging . . . learning how to 'relate'. . . . To live for the moment is the prevailing passion—to live for yourself, not for your predecessors or posterity. We are fast losing the sense of historical continuity. . . ." (September 30, 1976.)

I feel such estimation fails to acknowledge that our conventional lifestyle destroys our health and our spirit. It denatures us. How can we improve our lives "in ways that matter" when the cost of medical and health attention is beyond the financial capability of most Americans? When diet and nutrition have produced problems of epidemic levels; when stress has helped create a plague of cancer and heart disease; and when inflation stalks the domesticity of everyone? The common activity of daily life has become so electrified that even to remember predecessors or find a moment in which to contemplate posterity has become a luxury. Our psychic, social, and political conditions have gone berserk, and every well-meaning attempt to restore decency and sanity to our collective life is chewed in the maws of that madness, co-opted and perverted to the uses of the status quo.

I feel there is only one choice the thinking individual can make: go within. Go within and patiently rediscover the self. Without this return, the concerned individual melts into the computerized mass, the driven collections who are lost and do not know it. Spiritual explorers are concerned individuals. By responding to the doubts and feelings of our inner and outer being we instinctively begin to improve our conditions by assuming responsibility for who we are and how we live. This action determines the future of the individual, which, in turn, sets the tone of communal life.

Unified awareness offers alternative to any "stranger and afraid in a world I never made." It offers a natural spirituality that transcends the religiosity of ego. Natural spirituality can define your life and enable you to master the material world you live in, a world in which you visit and seek a way to grow. This is where you learn to live dual lives—one in the conditioned reality of the material world and the other as a free spirit of the cosmos. By unifying awareness you may hope to achieve your birthright as a child of god. Too many religious and psycho-spiritual systems call for various forms of surrender that are an integral and beneficial part of their method. However, these should be entered into—if you choose—only *after* your own unification, not in consequence of highly impressive exposures to powerful persons, sources, or forms. The way of surrender is real but it is a subtle path for which very few are suited.

Expanded consciousness grows from self-responsibility, discipline and careful, holistic practice. It does little good just to jog or eat a sound diet. By itself meditation may become a foil to the ego. Without a unified approach you are susceptible to disorientation in which time, direction, and energy are lost in confused shortcuts. There are no shortcuts; there is only patient, continuous practice.

Remember that meditation is an excellent means to explore the possibilities of understanding past lives, for the mind contains everything. Meditation clearly shows us how we are usually limited to a local awareness, a tiny patch of the vast domain of consciousness. The revelation of all that ever has been, is, and will be is blocked from the start because of our refusal to explore the mystery of death. In an age in which we can put men on the moon it is not too much to hope that our society will drop its taboos on death, easing the way for the spiritual explorer to reclaim death as part of the human experience. Left to ordinary awareness, we continue to fear death and refuse to explore its nature or prepare for its coming. How we live should determine the quality of our death as well as that of our life. Governed by the common politics of science and religion, by traditional authority, we fail to honor our calling as sentient beings.

Awareness does not need the sanction of science or religion, the authorization of a guru or master. You can develop awareness on your own and it will draw you to others who are so involved. As you develop you may decide to attend seminars, join meditation groups, or seek the company of those from whom you may gain insight and information. *Tread carefully.* Do not get attached and forget where the final responsibility lies. Be discriminating about wherein you put your trust. The most trustworthy of all is you, yourself, your intuitive inner essence.

The pursuit may be lonely at times, especially in the beginning. Some will not be as understanding as you wish. They may even feel angry or wounded, thinking that your attitudes implicitly condemn them. This is not so, cannot be so, for this path of awareness is founded on kindness and compassion. But you must attend to your self. From time to time you may find yourself surrounded by hostile vibrations put out by others. When you are in situations with people who cause or project negativity, remain calm. Generate positive energy to protect your own atmosphere, to keep negative vibrations from entering. Do not try to change anyone. Allow others to discover for themselves a need for other awareness. Eventually you will become a truer friend to all around you.

Perhaps because my job calls on me to attend to the needs and desires of others I particularly treasure solitude. I have grown to believe that we all need to know solitude; we all need times in which we organize quiet in order to establish our inner balance and become centered. In the beginning, living awareness is an uphill struggle. There is so much racket and rowdiness in the world and so much chatterbox monologing in one's own head. We need solitude and silence at regular and frequent intervals. The stillness becomes spacious, and in that infinite space we allow all and everything simply to be. Then all things reveal qualities we previously have missed. All of a sudden we may, if we are lucky, perceive that we are not separate from, but part of, all that surrounds us. The perception flees the very instant it is recognized.

I am alone yet not lonely. There are never enough hours for the walks I want to make, the books I want to read. In my journal I began to purge the layers of plastic personality, the fears locked inside. I began to see that the life I was living was a life I had always led and that it was not going to be substantially changed by death. All that I had done, all that I was doing, and all that I would do was a process of growth, an expansion of consciousness that was boundless. I discovered that my present was my past and future and they formed a concurrent existence that took me beyond all the previous borders. I was capable of endless recognitions. For the first time there was a harmony. I knew the meaning of peace and freedom when I realized that the veil of illusion under which I had once lived covered the simple tool of awareness.

Within each of us there is an endless well of energy that remains untapped.

Changing the style of one's life requires time and careful consideration, flexible yet persistent effort. Rigidity hinders growth and impedes the recognition of the self as a whole being alive with energy, light and love, vibrant with creativity and untold potential. It is not necessary to become a vegetarian or retire to an ashram or monastery. The true challenge lies in who you are and where you are in this moment, this present.

The key is to flow with the process of awareness and learn to trust the inner voice. Most importantly, learn to love and forgive yourself and rest assured that the negative past becomes positive food for development as you grow from new experience. You have evolved and will keep evolving. The essential is intangible and to perceive the intangible is what you are after. To live in harmony with both the material and spiritual aspects of your life requires courage, compassion, and patience. Courage to be different, to dissolve the attachments of materialism. Compassion for other people, other forms of life and for all things, and patience that arises from trusting in this path of wonder and change.

Bibliography

Ballentine, Rudolph. *Diet and Nutrition: A Holistic Approach*. Honesdale, Pa.: Himalayan International Institute, 1978.

Bateson, Gregory. *Steps to an Ecology of Mind*. New York: Ballantine Books, 1972.

Blofield, John. *Mantras: Sacred Words of Power*. New York: E. P. Dutton, 1977.

Boyd, Doug. *Rolling Thunder*. New York: Random House, 1974.

Boyd, Doug. *Swami*. New York: Random House, 1976.

Bucke, R. M. *Cosmic Consciousness*. New York: E. P. Dutton, 1960.

Campbell, Joseph. *Hero with a Thousand Faces*. New York: World Publishing Co. Reprint: Meridian Book Edition, 1956.

Campbell, Joseph. *The Masks of God: Creative Mythology*. New York: Viking Press, 1968

Cannon, Walter B. *The Wisdom of the Body*. New York: W. W. Norton, 1942.

Capra, Frijof. *The Tao of Physics*. Berkeley, Calif.: Shambhala, 1975.

Casteneda, Carlos. *The Teachings of Don Juan*. New York: Simon & Schuster, 1968.

Casteneda, Carlos. *A Separate Reality*. New York: Simon & Schuster, 1971.

Casteneda, Carlos. *Journey to Ixtlan*. New York: Simon & Schuster, 1972.

Casteneda, Carlos. *Tales of Power*. New York: Simon & Schuster, 1974.

Casteneda, Carlos. *The Second Ring of Power*. New York: Simon & Schuster,

de Chardin, P. Teilhard. *The Phenomenon of Man*. Translated by B. Wall. New York: Harper Torchbooks, 1961.

de Chardin, P. Teilhard. *Hymn of the Universe*. New York: Harper & Row, 1965.

de Chardin, Teilhard, *In Quest of the Perfection of Man*. New Jersey: Associated University Presses, 1973.

Cox, Harvey. *Turning East*. New York: Simon & Schuster, 1977.

de Ropp, Robert S. *Drugs and the Mind*. New York: Delacorte Press, 1957.

de Ropp, Robert S. *The Master Game*. New York: Delacorte Press, 1968.

de Ropp, Robert S. *Warrior's Way*. New York: Delacorte Press, 1979.

Dubos, Rene. *So Human An Animal*. New York: Charles Scribner's Sons, 1968.

Dufty, William. *Sugar Blues*. Radnor, Pa.: Chilton, 1975.

Easwaren, Eknath. *The Bhagavid Gita for Daily Living*. California: Blue Mountain Center of Meditation, 1975.

Ewald, Ellen Buchman. *Recipes for a Small Planet*. New York: Ballantine, 1973.

Feldenkrais, Moshe. *Awareness Through Movement*. New York: Harper & Row, 1972.

Goleman, Daniel. *The Varieties of the Meditative Experience*. New York: E. P. Dutton, 1977.

Grant, Joan. *Winged Pharaoh*. New York: Berkeley Publishing Corporation, 1937.

Green, Elmer and Green, Alyce. *Beyond Biofeedback*. New York: Delacorte Press, 1977.

Grossman, Richard. *Choosing and Changing*. New York: E. P. Dutton, 1978.

Gurdjieff, G. I. *Meetings with Remarkable Men*. New York: E. P. Dutton, 1963.

Haich, Elizabeth. *Initiation*. Palo Alto, Calif.: Seed Center, 1960.

Hesse, Hermann. *Steppenwolf*. New York: Bantam Books, 1963.

Huxley, Aldous. *The Doors of Perception*. New York: Harper & Row, 1954.

Jackson, Mildred, and Teague, Terri. *The Handbook of Alternatives to Chemical Medicine*. Oakland, Calif.: Lawton-Teague Publications, 1975.

Jung, C. J. *Psychological Reflections*. New York: Harper & Row, 1953.

Kapleau, P. *Three Pillars of Zen*. Boston: Beacon Press, 1967.

Kapleau, Phillip, ed. *The Wheel of Death: A Collection of Writings from Zen Buddhist and Other Sources on Death-Rebirth-Dying*. New York: Harper & Row, 1971.

Keen, Sam. *Voices and Visions*. New York: Harper & Row, 1970.

Keleman, Stanley. *Living Your Dying*. New York: Random House/Bookworks, 1974.

Keleman, Stanley. *The Human Ground*. California: Science and Behaviour Books, Inc., 1975.

Keleman, Stanley. *Your Body Speaks Its Mind*. New York: Simon & Schuster, 1975.

Krishna, Gopi. *The Awakening of Kundalini*. New York: E. P. Dutton, 1975.

Lappe, Frances Moore. *Diet for a Small Planet*. New York: Ballantine, 1971.

Leonard, George. *The Silent Pulse*. New York: E. P. Dutton, 1978.

Le Shan, Lawrence. *How to Meditate*. New York: Bantam, 1975.

Lindbergh, Anne Morrow. *Gift from the Sea*. New York: Vintage Books, A Division of Random House, 1955.

Luce, Gay. *Your Second Life*. New York: Delacorte Press, 1979.

Ludeman, Kay, and Henderson, Louise. *Resource Handbook on Allergies*. Dallas: Ludeman & Henderson, 1978.

Maters, R. E., and Houston, J. *Varieties of Psychedelic Experience*. New York: Holt, Rinehart & Winston, 1966.

Maugham, W. Somerset. *The Razor's Edge*. New York: Pocket Books, Inc., 1944.

McCartney, James. *Yoga, The Key to Life*. New York: E. P. Dutton, 1969.

Miller, Roberta DeLong. *Psychic Massage*. New York: Harper & Row, 1975.

Moody, Raymond, A., Jr., M.D. *Life after Life*. New York: Bantam, 1975.

Muktananda. *Selected Essays*. Edited by Paul Zweig. New York: Harper & Row, 1976.

Ornstein, Robert, E. ed. *The Nature of Human Consciousness*. San Francisco: W. H. Freeman, 1973.

Pearce, Joseph Chilton. *Exploring the Crack in the Cosmic Egg*. New York: Julian Press, 1974.

Pelletier, Kenneth R. *Holistic Medicine*. New York: Delacorte Press, 1979.

Pelletier, Kenneth R. *Mind as Healer, Mind as Slayer: A Holistic Approach to Preventing Stress Disorders*. New York: Delacorte Press, 1977.

Pelletier, Kenneth R. *Toward a Science of Consciousness*. New York: Delacorte Press, 1978.

Pelletier, Kenneth R., and Garfield, Charles. *Consciousness: East and West*. New York: Harper & Row, 1976.

Rajneesh, Bhagwan Shree. *The Book of Secrets*. New York: Harper & Row, 1974.

Rajneesh, Bhagwan Shree. *Only One Sky*. New York: E. P. Dutton, 1975.

Reinhold, H. A. ed. *The Soul Afire: Revelations of the Mystics*. Meridian Books, 1944.

Robertson, Laurel; Flinders; Carol and Godfrey, Bronwen. *Laurel's Kitchen: A Handbook for Vegetarian Cookery and Nutrition*. Berkeley, Calif.: Nilgiri Press, 1976.

Roszak, Theodore. *Person/Planet*. Garden City, N.Y.: Doubleday & Co., 1979.

Roszak, Theodore. *Unfinished Animal*. New York: Harper & Row, 1975.

Schwarz, Jack. *Human Energy Systems*. New York, E. P. Dutton, 1979.

Schwarz, Jack. *The Path of Action*. New York: E. P. Dutton, 1977.

Schwarz, Jack. *Voluntary Controls*. New York: E. P. Dutton, 1978.

Smith, Huston. *Forgotten Truth: The Primordial Tradition*. New York: Harper & Row, 1976.

Trungpa, Chogyam. *Glimpses of Abhidharma*. Boulder, Co.: Prajna Press, 1978.

Trungpa, Chogyam. *Meditation in Action*. Berkeley, Calif: Shambhala, 1970.

Tulkum Tarthang (Ed.). *Reflections of Mind*. Berkeley, Calif.: Dharma Publishing Co., 1975.

Weil, Andrew. *The Natural Mind: A New Way of Looking at Drugs and the Higher Consciousness*. Boston: Houghton Mifflin, 1972.

Wilhelm, R. *The I Ching or Book of Changes*. Princeton, N.J.: Princeton University Press, 1967.

Wilson, Colin. *The Outsider*. Boston: Houghton Mifflin, 1956.

Wilson, Colin. *The Occult*. New York: Vintage Books, 1971.

Wilson, Colin. *Strange Powers*. New York: Random House, 1973.

Yogananda, Paramahansa. *The Science of Religion*. California: Self-Realization Fellowship, 1953.

Young, Arthur M. *The Bell Notes*. New York: Delacorte Press, 1979.

Young, Arthur M. *The Geometry of Meaning*. New York: Delacorte Press, 1976.

Young, Arthur M. *The Reflexive Universe*. New York: Delacorte Press, 1976.

Yutang, Lin. *The Wisdom of China and India*. New York: Random House, 1942.